LET'S SIGN SCIENCE

BSL Vocabulary for Key Stage 1, 2 & 3

CATH SMITH and CLARE INGLE

Illustrated by Cath Smith

CO-SIGN COMMUNICATIONS

Incorporating Deafsign.com and DeafBooks.co.uk

FROM CO-SIGN COMMUNICATIONS (inc DeafBooks.co.uk)

LET'S SIGN DICTIONARY EVERYDAY BSL: 2nd Edition Revised & Enlarged

LET'S SIGN POCKET DICTIONARY: BSL Concise Beginner's Guide

OUR SCHOOL SIGNS: British Sign Language Vocabulary

LET'S SIGN BSL Greetings Signs & Fingerspelling A2 Wallchart

LET'S SIGN BSL Poster/Mats A4 Set of 4
Greetings-Family-Feelings-Questions

LET'S SIGN FOR WORK: BSL Guide for Service Providers **2nd Edition**

SIGN LANGUAGE LINK: A Pocket Dictionary of Signs

LET'S SIGN FAMILY TOPICS: BSL for Children and their Carers

EARLY YEARS

LET'S SIGN EARLY YEARS: BSL Child and Carer Guide **2nd Edition**

LET'S SIGN BSL EARLY YEARS & BABY SIGNS: Poster/Mats A3 Set of 2

LET'S SIGN BSL: EARLY YEARS CURRICULUM TUTOR BOOK

LET'S SIGN BSL: EARLY YEARS CURRICULUM STUDENT BOOK

FLASHCARDS

LET'S SIGN BSL: Early Years & Baby Signs FLASHCARDS

LET'S SIGN BSL: FEELINGS & EMOTIONS FLASHCARDS

LET'S SIGN BSL: CHRISTMAS SIGNS FLASHCARDS

LET'S SIGN BSL: FOOTBALL SIGNS FLASHCARDS

LET'S SIGN BSL : House & Home FLASHCARDS

LET'S SIGN BSL THANK YOU CARDS

LET'S SIGN SONGS FOR CHILDREN: Popular Songs to Sign-a-long to

LET'S SIGN & DOWN SYNDROME: Signs for Children with Special Needs

LET'S SIGN SCIENCE: BSL Vocabulary for KS 1, 2, & 3 (Dictionary)

A CHILD'S BOOK OF SIGNED PRAYERS

LET'S SIGN BSL REWARD STICKERS

(Many of the above publications are also now available in electronic and mobile applications and Kindle format)

GRAPHICS PACKS
On annual licences for creating your own materials

see www.Widgit.com

LET'S SIGN BSL: Full Adult Dictionary Set Graphics Pack

LET'S SIGN BSL: Baby & Early Years Graphics Pack

LET'S SIGN SCIENCE: BSL (KS 1, 2, & 3) Graphics Pack

ACKNOWLEDGEMENTS

My grateful thanks and appreciation to Clare Ingle, Teacher of the deaf and Valerie Helliwell, BSL Tutor, for allowing me to use and build on their original work on Science Sign Vocabulary for Bedfordshire Service for Sensory Impairment and Communication Difficulties (now Luton Education Authority).

And to Clare Ingle for steadfastly checking and rechecking drawings and coming back with notes and descriptions to help with changes.

To Liz Lawrence, Advisory Teacher for Primary Science and Technology, London Borough of Barking and Dagenham - a big thank you for sharing the core vocabulary wordlist for teaching Science terms.

To Bridget Payne and Kath Keogan for their support and being available to run things by from time to time.

For help with converting and developing illustrations for the LET'S SIGN & WRITE BSL Graphics packs, to Widgit Software Ltd.

For preparing the books for publication, innovating new working methods, and printing;

Stephen Smith, County Durham.

And to a very dear friend and colleague, Keith Williams of Cleveland Deaf community, who sadly died in September 2007. Keith was part of the Cleveland BSL tutor group - a group of committed individuals who have been involved at various stages in the development work on the graphics and publications that form the Let's Sign Series. Keith always gave generously of his time and expertise with good humour and encouragement for the work - he is greatly missed.

First published 2008

Reprinted 2013, 2015, 2017, 2018

ISBN-10: 1-905913-08-7

ISBN-13: 978-1-905913-08-4

Published by Co-Sign Communications
Incorporating Deafsign and DeafBooks
Stockton-on-Tees TS18 5HH
Tel: 01642 580505
email: cath@deafsign.com - info@deafbooks.co.uk

www.DeafBooks.co.uk

Printed through Amazon Print on Demand

CONTENTS

INTRODUCTION

This publication has evolved from the work carried out initially by Clare Ingle and Valerie Helliwell on a booklet of 310 descriptions for British Sign Language (BSL) vocabulary that they had developed to deliver the science curriculum to their pupils at a time when BSL materials for this subject were virtually non-existent.

The collection has been illustrated and expanded from various sources to also meet the needs of teachers and pupils at Key Stages 1 and 2 and now contains 720 signs.

Approximately 540 are 'science' related with 180 'general everyday' signs added to provide some basic examples for the main concepts in the schemes of work and units for Key Stages 1 and 2, in a single reference book. A fuller source of sign vocabulary and regional variations are available in the Let's Sign dictionaries and graphics packs to further support this wide subject area.

This resource is intended to offer support for teachers to deliver the ***National Curriculum programme of study** in line with the exemplar scheme that is aimed at offering opportunities for children to:

- *develop knowledge and understanding of important scientific ideas, processes and skills and relate these to everyday experiences;*
- *learn about ways of thinking and of finding out about and communicating ideas;*
- *explore values and attitudes through science.*

Such work requires the language and ability to communicate the ideas and concepts involved, and we hope that this book provides a useful reference for all those who use sign language to achieve this end.

This is not a definitive list of science terms but we believe that this book contains a **good basic core vocabulary** that demonstrates the visually structured nature of BSL and how this can be brought to scientific concepts. Our materials are intended to support BSL training and development in the hands of native Deaf sign language users - some recent projects can be found in Useful Resources on page 95.

BSL resources and materials for this important curriculum subject are still scant, with no standardisation for educational use. It is not easy to find science signs that have consensus of use from the sources available, and in practice, signs in education vary widely, with teachers left to invent signs on the spot when necessary.

The book includes more than one version of some signs to give choice if there is no clear consensus, or to suit different contexts, or to suit individual student needs at different stages. Some regional variations are covered, including compounds in which part of the sign is regional.

The writers also wish to point out that fingerspelling plays an important role in familiarising learners with the words that match the signs as would be required for use in examinations and future reading and study.

We include signs to encourage awareness of global issues and climate change. and we also encourage the use of paperless materials by our developments in electronic format with Kindle ebooks and downloadable resources to print or simply view on screen or whiteboard.

See **www.deafbooks.co.uk** and **www.widgit.com**

* http://www.standards.dfes.gov.uk/schemes2/science/teaching 'Teaching Science at key stages 1 & 2'

LET'S SIGN BSL GRAPHICS PACKS

The Let's Sign graphics are being continually developed to provide vocabulary needed by families, teachers, tutors and others involved with deaf children and adults and all sign language users who want to be involved.

This dictionary is one in our series of print publications that can be used as stand-alone items, or linked to, and supported by, other items in the series - all are intended to support BSL learning through courses designed for that purpose.

The signs are also available on annually renewable licences for teachers and families to create their own materials, see www.widgit.com/bsl for details.

The graphics are available in line and colour versions. They can be used within Widgit software such as Communicate InPrint 3, InPrint 2 and SymWriter to quickly and easily create BSL materials. They can also be used as clip-art graphics and incorporated into most standard applications such as Word and Powerpoint for making tailor-made materials for use by all those who use or teach BSL.

USING THE LET'S SIGN GRAPHICS IN STANDARD APPLICATIONS

When using the graphics packs it is important to note that the graphics are in folders and that each graphic has a single 'file name'. These can be viewed alphabetically on screen by opening the folder and choosing 'thumbnails 'in the View menu option. They can be selected and imported in the usual way into a document.

This dictionary has a full Index to help identify and locate signs that are needed, and to provide extra information and descriptions of the signs.

BAR GRAPH

GRAPH POINTS

LINE GRAPH

PLOT (on a graph)

TABLE, GRAPH

Signs in the dictionary are also entered alphabetically as in the examples above and most of the topic specific entries have the corresponding file name in the folders. However, many everyday signs have more than a single English word equivalent - and numerous English words have different ways of being signed depending on meaning in context.

The Index should enable you to locate the sign you want even if you are using a different name for the sign or looking for a term that is not the graphic's file name.

LOCATING SIGNS IN THE FOLDERS AND IN THE DICTIONARY

Because each sign has only a single entry and a single file name to identify it in the folders, it is important to be aware that the sign you are looking for could be named any one of a number of English word equivalents, and you will need to check the folder for words of similar meanings and cross check with the dictionary.

Similarly in the dictionary, to avoid multiple entries of the same sign, the headings and captions may contain additional meanings of the sign and these can be searched for alphabetically in the Index.

EXAMPLE 1

DARK, EVENING, NIGHT

Palm back hands swing in/down to finish crossed. Also means **DARKNESS**.

(File name in the folder 'night')

If you need a sign for DARK, the index will lead you to the sign in the dictionary with the heading - DARK, EVENING, NIGHT.

In the graphics folders, this sign has the file name NIGHT, so you can then look through the graphic files using the meanings from the headings to find this graphic.

If you are seeking the sign NIGHT, you can locate it by that name in the folder, and the book index will lead you to this same entry in the dictionary, so that you can check for other meanings and the description of movement.

EXAMPLE 2

If you are looking for a sign for REGULAR, you would find the dictionary page entry under ALWAYS, REGULAR with the additional meaning USUAL added in the caption.

Using these words to check the graphic files, you would find this sign under the file name ALWAYS.

ALWAYS, REGULAR

Extended R. thumb moves to the right/forward behind L. flat hand held palm back/right. Also means **USUAL.**

(File name in the folder 'always')

NUMBERS: Quick Reference Guide

Numbers are notorious for their regional variations and there are many more than is possible to show in this simple guide. The examples below are based on the two systems most commonly used and understood in this country. Learners need to know their own regional signs and also to be aware of those used in other areas. Tutors are welcome to submit details of other variations to the contact details at the bottom of the page, and it may be possible to include them in future editions.

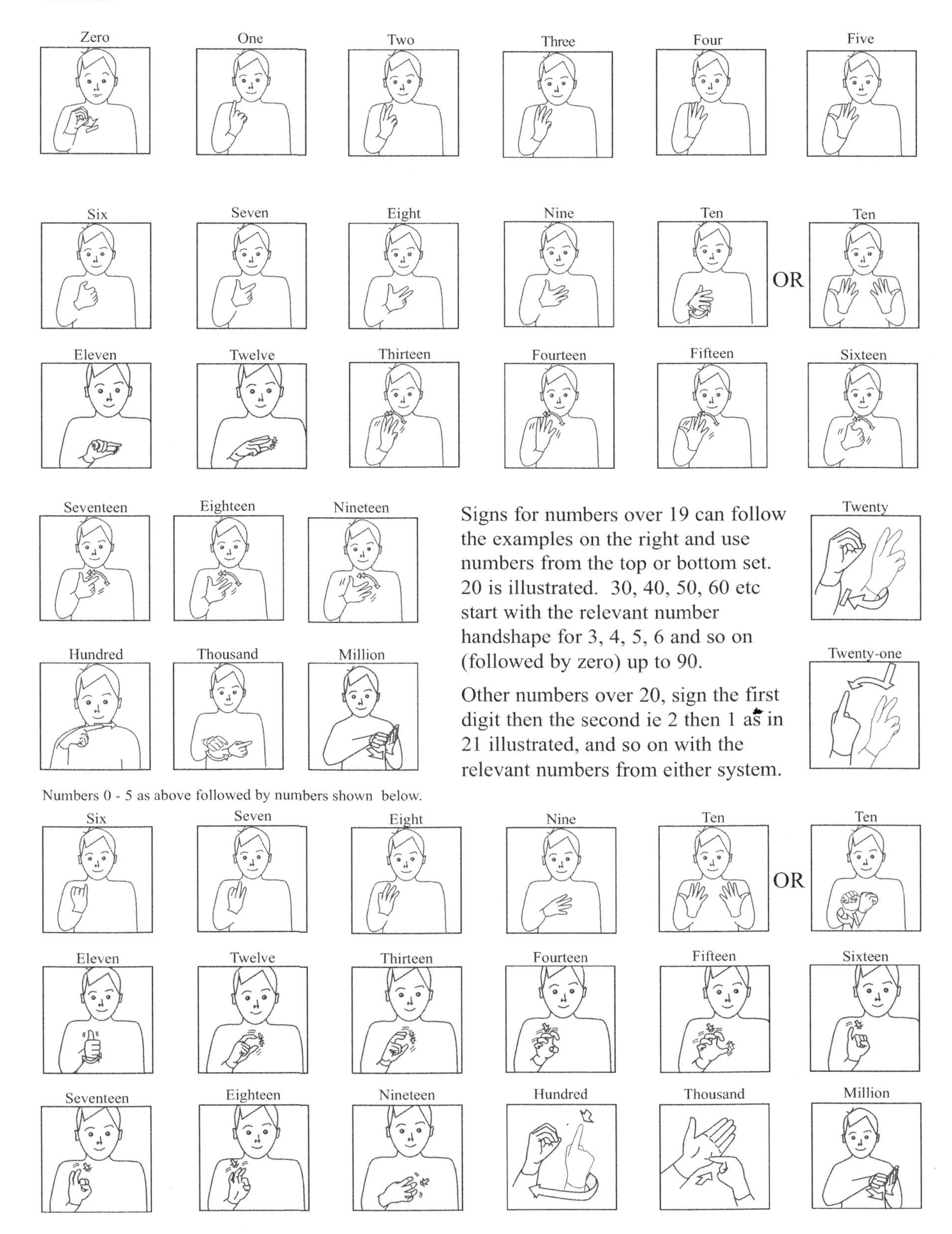

Signs for numbers over 19 can follow the examples on the right and use numbers from the top or bottom set. 20 is illustrated. 30, 40, 50, 60 etc start with the relevant number handshape for 3, 4, 5, 6 and so on (followed by zero) up to 90.

Other numbers over 20, sign the first digit then the second ie 2 then 1 as in 21 illustrated, and so on with the relevant numbers from either system.

GUIDE TO DICTIONARY HEADINGS AND CAPTIONS

Words and signs may not have direct equivalent matches, but signs are identified in the headings with their main meaning or meanings with some added in the captions, so the Index should be used to check all possible entries of the sign/word needed. In this publication the meanings ascribed are relevant to the science curriculum and may not always be appropriate to other contexts.

The words give each sign's main meaning or meanings separated by commas such as BATTERY, ELECTRIC/ITY, and sometimes include the commonly used parts of a word that may be used when people search - for example COMPARE, COMPARISON. Where space is limited, part words are sometimes abbreviated such as CONNECT/ION and ELECTRIC/ITY.

The captions give extra information on the handshape, orientation, location and movement of signs.

Details of non-manual features ***(facial/bodily expressions) variation,*** and changes in ***context*** are given in ***bold italics*** when relevant and where space allows. Additional meanings are given in **BOLD CAPITALS**.

Most signs are drawn as if you are looking at the signer. The signs are always depicted as if the signer is right-handed with the right hand always referred to as R. and the left hand as L. in the captions.

Left-handed signers will use the reverse of this, with the left hand as dominant.

From the thumb, the fingers are referred to as index, middle, ring and little finger.

Orientation, direction and movement

The direction the hands may face, point or move are described as if the hands are open, with orientation based on the way the palm faces regardless of whether the hand is open or closed.

The hands may be described as '*pointing*' up, forward etc even if the fingers are bent in a different direction or closed.

As illustrated above, the R. hand is palm left and the L. hand is palm right.

They can also be described as palm facing, or palm in.

This example would be described as two fists held side by side, pointing forward, palms facing.

If the handshapes are described for example as *index, and thumb extended*, then it is understood that the other fingers are closed.

Diagonal movements are described '*forward/left*' or '*back/right*' and so on.

BSL HANDSHAPES

These are some of the frequently used handshapes in BSL and the terms used in this book to describe them.

Fist

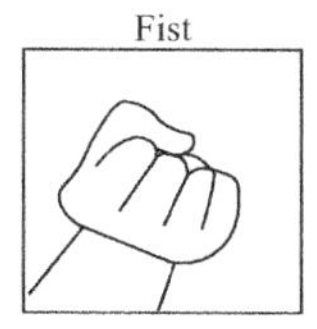

The hand is tightly closed and the thumb is across the fingers.

Bunched Hand

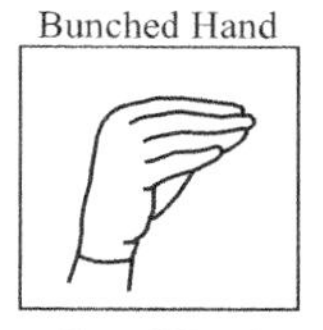

The finger ends and thumb are bunched together.

Closed Hand

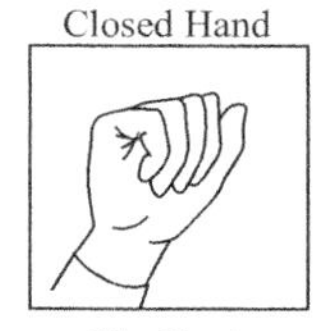

The hand is closed and the thumb is against the index finger.

Flat Hand

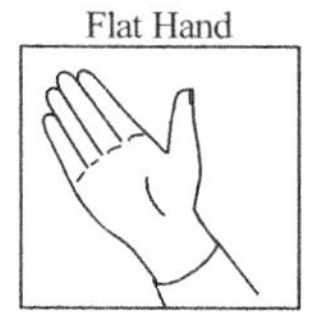

The fingers are straight and together.

'L' Hand

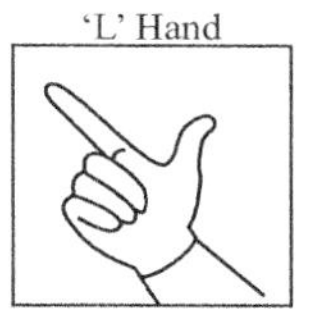

The hand is closed with the index finger and thumb extended in an 'L' shape.

'C' Hand

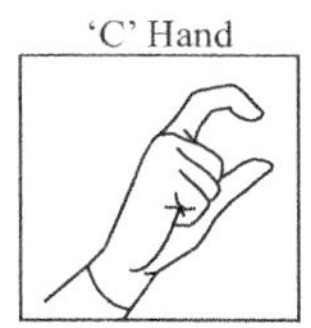

The hand is closed with the index finger and thumb extended and curved in a 'C' shape.

'O' Hand

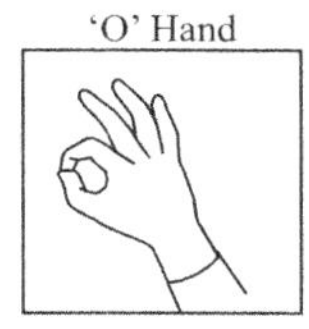

The tip of the index finger touches the tip of the thumb to form an 'O' shape.

'M' Hand

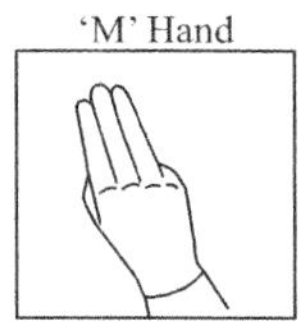

The index, middle and ring fingers are extended, straight and held together.

'V' Hand

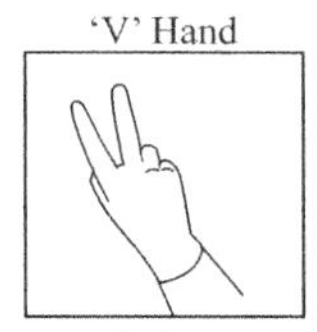

The index and middle fingers are extended and spread apart.

Index

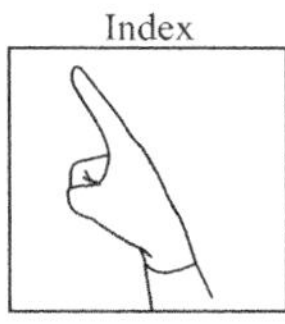

The index finger is extended from a closed hand.

Clawed Hand

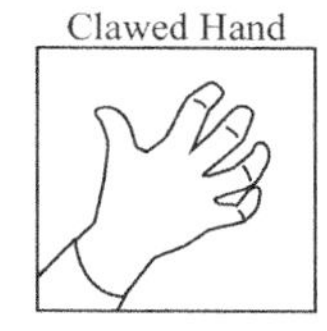

The fingers are extended and bent and spread apart.

Bent Hand

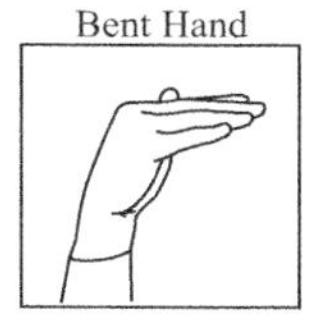

The fingers are straight, and together and bent at the palm knuckles.

Irish 'T' Hand

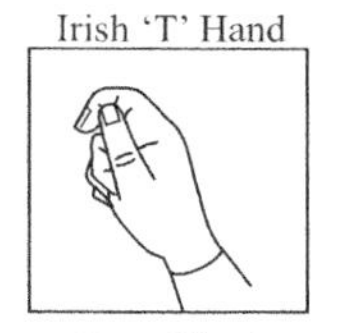

(From 'T' in Irish fingerspelling)
The hand is closed with the index finger bent round the top of the thumb.

Open Hand

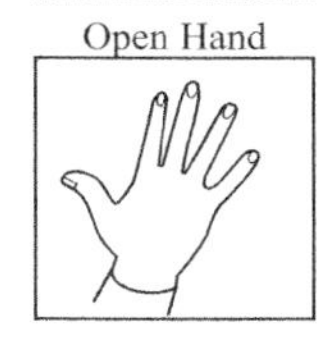

The fingers and thumb are straight and spread apart.

'Y' Hand

The hand is closed with the little finger and thumb extended.

Full 'C' Hand

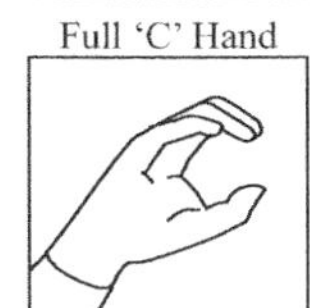

The thumb is curved and fingers are together and curved in a 'C' shape.

Full 'O' Hand

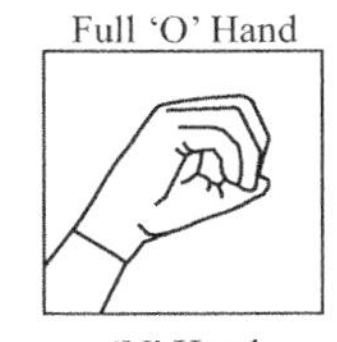

The tips of fingers and thumb are held together to form an 'O' shape.

'N' Hand

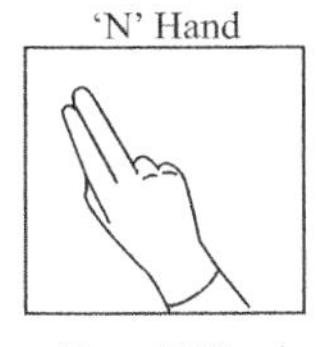

The index and middle fingers are extended, together and straight.

Bent 'V Hand

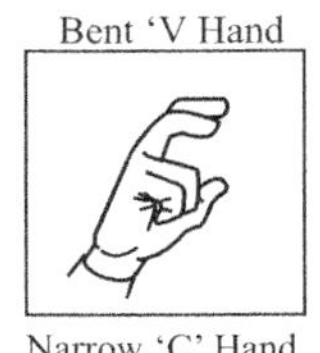

The bent index and middle fingers are extended from a fist and spread apart.

Narrow 'C' Hand

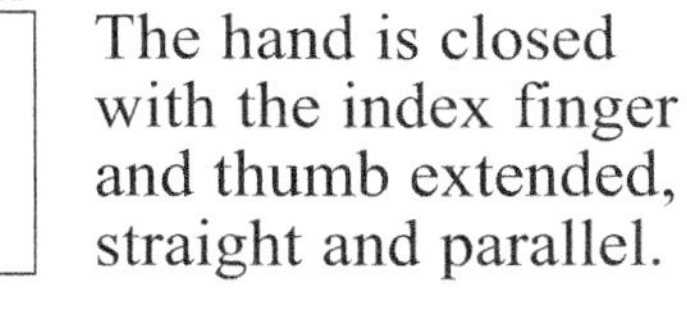

The hand is closed with the index finger and thumb extended, straight and parallel.

GUIDE TO DRAWINGS: BSL FEATURES

The signs contained in this book show numerous examples of the ways in which underlying concepts and meanings can be embedded into sign units through the visual, gestural and spatial grammatical features of BSL. Awareness of these elements can help in understanding sign formations and be further used in the teaching of this subject.

BSL incorporates a range of specific lip-patterns, eye, mouth and facial expressions (non-manual features) that can add, modify or change meaning. In addition, signs that have a number of English equivalent meanings can be distinguished by their word lip-patterns. All of these features are best seen in real life demonstration or video clips such as those referenced in Useful Resources on page 95.

In simple line drawings such as these, it is difficult to do justice to these aspects but the drawings do show the main features with further details in the captions where space allows.

Where the drawings show a start and end position, the hands at the beginning of the movement are shown in a slightly lighter line.

The examples shown above incorporate the non-manual features of sucked in cheeks to convey the idea of something being drawn in or towards, eg. (from the left) **MAGNETISM** - an aspect that is emphasised further by the addition of open hands closing in **ABSORB/TAKE UP,** and **VACUUM.**

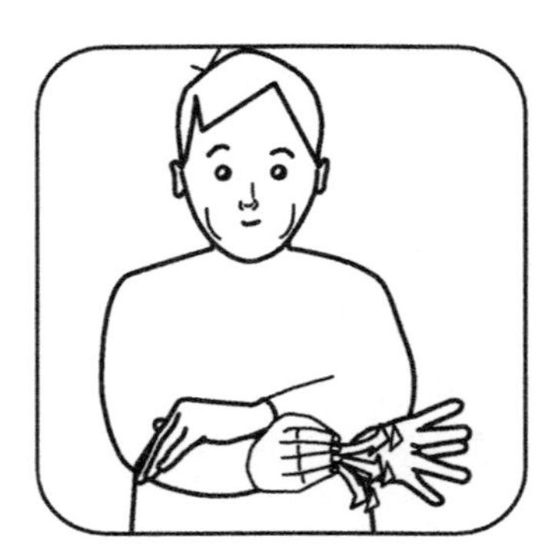

In the next examples, puffed cheeks often occur in signs to show intensity, such as in **EMISSIONS/POLLUTION, PRESSURE, FAT/OBESE** and so on.

Some signs are based on compounding in which separate ideas are brought together. Some examples here (left to right) include **WORK+START = ACTIVATE, LIGHT+MAKE = PHOTOSYNTHESIS, FARM+ANIMAL = LIVESTOCK.** Some are shown as separate signs in the same box and others are incorporated into one sign.

Again, the lighter line shows the start of the sign and the darker shows the finish. Some components may vary regionally and many samples are included. In addition, the captions give the separate units of meaning in brackets where there is space, to allow for modifications for regional differences.

A time line from over the right shoulder gives a useful reference for long passages of time, or going back a long way as in **HEREDITARY, ANCESTORS** and **EVOLUTION.**

Headnod and headshake can be used to reinforce positive statements, or change them to a negative as in **SOLUBLE** and **INSOLUBLE** and again in the sign on the right, changing the sign **NORMAL** to the negative **ABNORMAL**.

Such factors have the effect of compacting meaning into the sign units and this is an important feature of BSL.

FINGERSPELLING

Fingerspelling is an integral part of BSL and can be incorporated into or form the basis of some signs and used to spell words in full.

Initial letters are particularly useful in sign formations.

The examples here show **AMMETER, DILUTE, CATALYST** and **VITAMIN** and there are many more examples throughout the book.

Many small words such as **ACID, CELL, GAS, MASS, PREY,** and so on, can be fingerspelt in full.

AMMETER

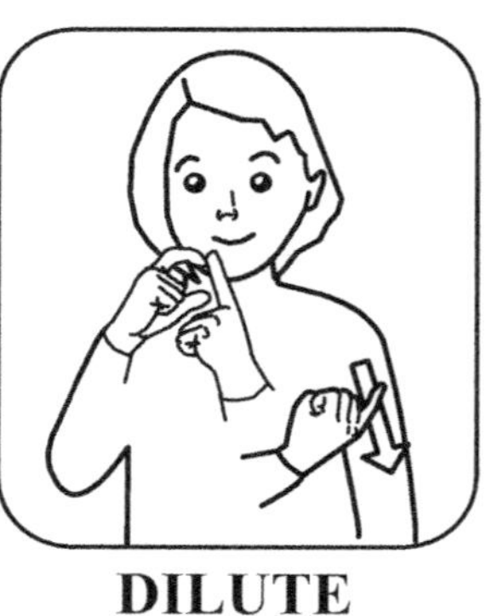

DILUTE

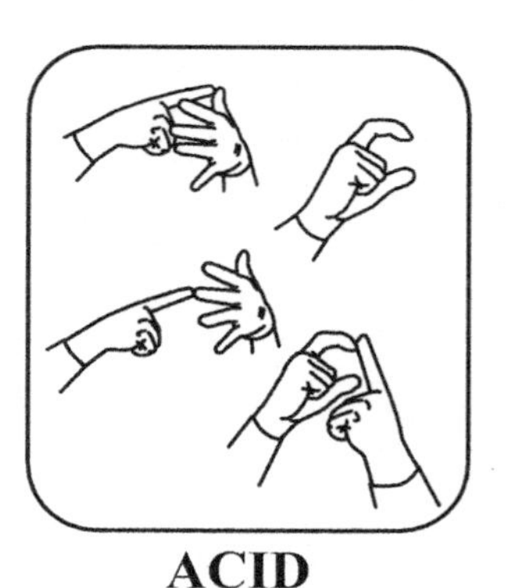

ACID

CATALYST

VITAMIN

Full colour A4 charts for right and left-handed fingerspelling alphabets are available as free downloads from **www.deafbooks.co.uk/downloads**
Downloads also include Winter Weather and Numbers Quick Reference Guide.

AIDS

(Auto Immune Deficiency Syndrome) R. index finger held across backs of L. 'V' fingers, taps twice. **HIV** is usually fingerspelt.

ABNORMAL

R. hand of fingerspelt 'N' formation brushes forwards off L. palm twice as the head shakes, lips pressed together.

ABORTION

Spread fingers of R. hand on abdomen move out as fingers close (**TAKE AWAY, REMOVE**).

ABOUT, APPROXIMATELY

Palm down open hand moves round in horizontal circles. The mouth is closed and lips pushed forward slightly.

ABSORB, TAKE UP

Open hands held forward in front of body pull back/up to chest as fingers close onto thumbs, with cheeks sucked in. ***Directional.***

ABSORBENT

Fingers of R. hand close onto thumb as hand moves back/upwards under palm down L. hand. Cheeks are sucked in.

ACCELERATION

Fingerspell 'A' then R. index taps up and down quickly off L. several times (**FAST**).

ACID (chemical)

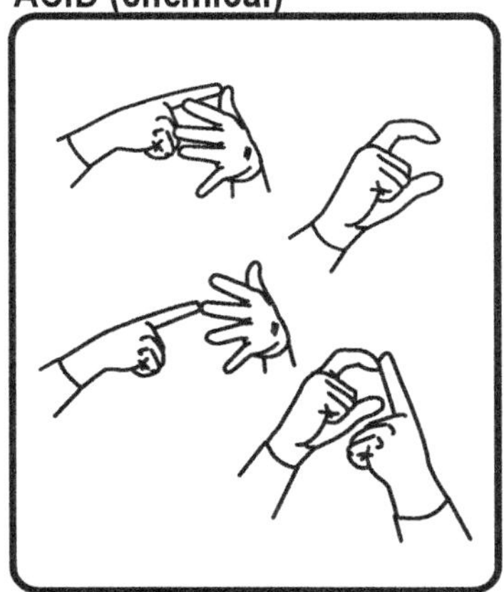

Fingerspell 'A' 'C' 'I' 'D'.

ACID (taste), SOUR

Tip of extended little finger touches lower lip and moves sharply away to the side.

ACTION, WORK

Edge of R. flat hand makes short forward chopping movements on L. at right angles.

ACTIVATE

R. flat hand chops edge down on L. at right angles (**WORK**) then closed hand with thumb up moves sharply down behind L. (**START**).

ADULT, GROWN-UP

Bent hand moves firmly upwards near head height. Also means **TALL**.

AERIAL

Extended R. index finger points and moves towards L. upright index, and moves back again.

AEROPLANE, FLY, FLIGHT

Closed hand with thumb and little finger extended moves in action of a plane flying.

AIM, TARGET

R. flat hand moves forward towards extended L. index finger held forward.

AIR PRESSURE

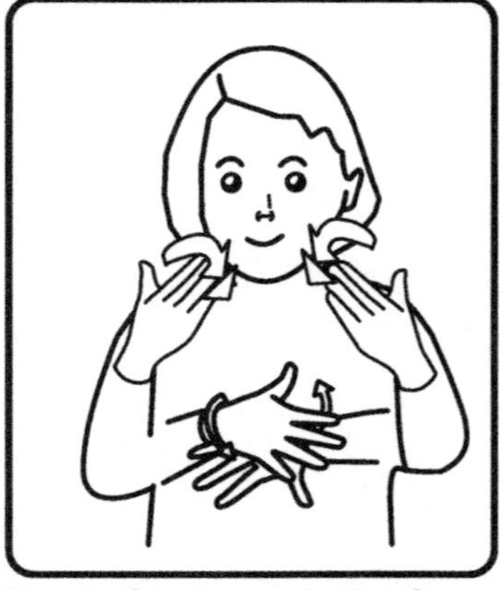

Hands fan towards the face (**AIR**) then palm to palm open hands press down firmly or with a slight twist (**PRESS**).

AIR, BREEZE

Palm back flat hands make fanning movements near the face.

ALARM, BELL

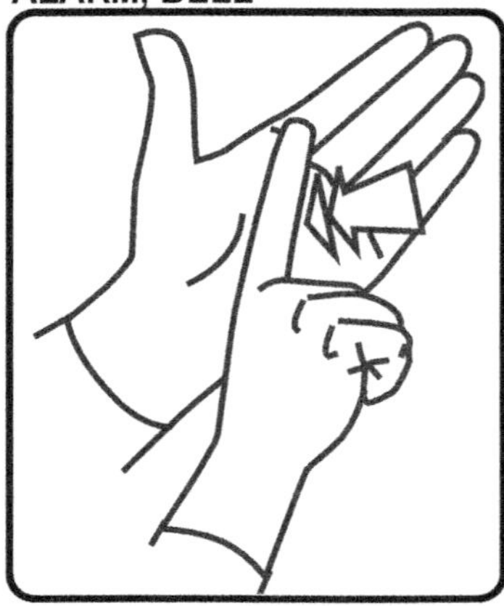

Side of extended R. index finger bangs twice against the L. palm. Index waggles forward/down for **CLOCK.**

ALCOHOL

(Organic compound containing one or more OH groups) Fingerspell 'O' 'H'.

ALCOHOL, BEER, DRINK

Full 'C' hand moves in horizontal circles in front of the mouth.

ALIVE, LIFE, LIVE

Tip of middle finger (or clawed hand) rubs up and down on side of chest.

ALKALI, ALKALINE

(Having the properties of a base with a pH of more than 7) Fingerspell 'A' 'L' 'K' or the whole word.

ALLERGY, ALLERGIC

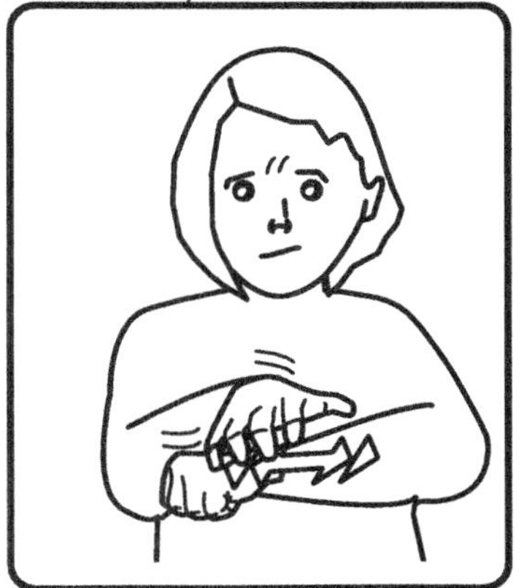

Tips of clawed hand rub in scratching action on arm, or appropriate part of body.

ALTOGETHER, COMPLETE

Palm forward open hands with fingers curved twist down and round to contact, closing to bunched hands.

ALWAYS, REGULAR

Extended R. thumb moves to the right/forward behind L. flat hand held palm back/right. Also means **USUAL.**

AMMETER

Fingerspelt 'A' followed by R. extended index finger swinging to and fro against L. palm, like a needle on a meter.

ANALOGUE

R. extended index finger moves to the right in up and down wavy movements away from L. index.

ANCESTORS

Fingerspelt 'F' formation moves forward/down in small hops from over right shoulder. Also means **INHERITED, PEDIGREE**.

ANIMAL

Clawed hands make repeated forward circular movements. Also means **CRAWL.**

ANODE

Extended index fingers held at right angles (**POSITIVE**), then fingerspell 'A' and finish with indexes pointing down (**ELECTRODE**).

ANT

Fingers of R. clawed hand wiggle up the left forearm.

APPARATUS

Fingerspell 'A' 'P' 'P' then edges of closed hands with index fingers up bang together twice (**THINGS**).

AREA, AROUND

Palm down R. open hand moves in circles above L. upright index. Also means **LOCAL, PLACE, REGION, SITUATION, SURROUNDING.**

AREA, LOCAL, PLACE

Palm down open hand makes horizontal circular movements. Also means **REGION, SITUATION.**

ARM

R. index finger points to left arm.

ARTERY

Fingerspell 'A' then index finger on chest moves out/down away from the heart in repeated movement.

ATMOSPHERE

Palm up open hands make upward circular fanning movements at head height.

ATOM

Fingerspell 'A' then form 'O' hand with R. index finger contacting thumb or fingerspell the full word.

ATTRACT, ATTRACTION

(General term eg. bees attracted to flowers)
'O' hand pulls forward from the front of the chest.

AUTUMN

Fingers of R. hand wiggle as hand moves down at side of L. hand in formation of sign for ***TREE***.

AVERAGE, MEAN

Palm down flat hands held together sweep round in large horizontal circle. Also means **EQUAL, STANDARD.**

AXIS

(Eg. axis of rotation - the polar diameter of the earth)
Tips of index fingers touch, hands held at an angle.

BACTERIA

Fingerspell 'B' then palm down open hands move forward/out, fingers wiggling (**SPREAD**).

BACTERIUM

Tips of 'O' hands in contact, then R. hand moves away to the right in small twisting movements from the wrist.

BADGER

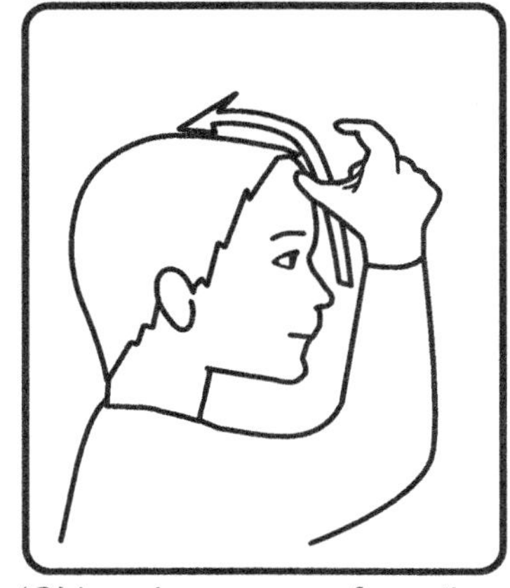

'C' hand moves up from the nose and backwards across top of head to indicate the white stripe.

BAR GRAPH

L. hand held in 'L' formation; R. hand with index and thumb in narrow 'C' hand moves down then repeats, moving to the right.

BAT

Fingers of R. bent 'V' hand hook onto L. 'N' hand or the sign ***WINGS*** also sometimes used.

BATTERY, ELECTRIC/ITY

Tips of bent 'V' hand tap twice against front of chin. **ELECTRIC** and **ELECTRICITY** have other ***regional variations.***

BEAK, EAGLE

Palm left R. 'C' hand moves forward/down from nose as fingers close together. Also signed with palm forward curved index from nose.

BEAKER

R. clawed hand (or full 'C' hand) moves upwards from palm up L. hand.

BEE, FLY

'O' hand moves forward/left with small quick twisting movements from the wrist.

BEND, BENDY

Irish 'T hands twist from wrists in bending action. Closed or bunched hands can also be used.

BICYCLE, BIKE, CYCLE

Closed hands (or bent index fingers) make alternate forward circular motions. Also means **PEDAL.**

BIOLOGY

Fingerspell 'B' then tip of middle finger rubs up and down on side of chest (**LIFE**).

BIRD, BEAK

Index finger and thumb open and close in front of mouth. Elbows may move in and out (**CHICKEN**).

BIRTHDAY

Flat hands near sides of waist move forward/in and then upwards and apart. ***Varies.***

BLOOD

R. index finger brushes bottom lip (**RED**) then R. palm down open hand brushes forward across back of L. (may repeat).

BLOOD PRESSURE

R. clawed hand grasps left upper arm, then moves slightly away and makes repeated squeezing action.

BLOOD SAMPLE

Back of R. 'V' hand rests against left arm, then pulls away as fingers close onto thumb.

BLOW BUBBLES

Blow towards Irish 'T' hand held near mouth, then full 'O' hand opens and closes several times, moving up and away.

BODY

Flat hands move down sides of body.

BODY, ANATOMY

Palm back open hands contact upper chest, then repeat, moving downwards.

BOILING POINT

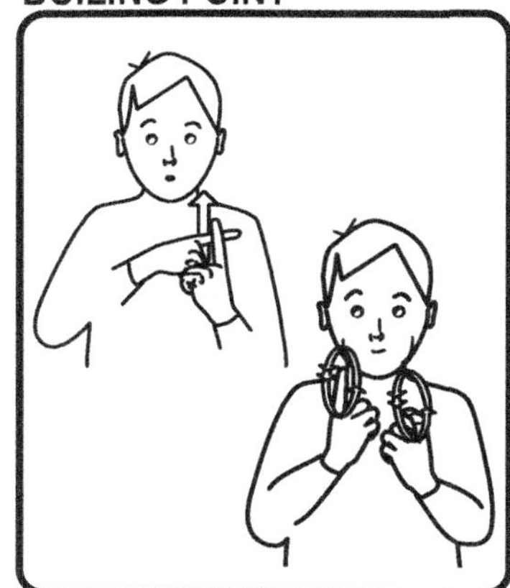

R. index moves up behind L. at right angle (**TEMPERATURE**) then index fingers flick up in small alternate circles (**BOIL, BOILING**).

BONE

Tips of 'C' hand move down appropriate part of body.
Varies.

BONE

Knuckles of R. closed hand rap against the left elbow.
Varies.

BOY

Extended R. index finger brushes across chin to the left. May repeat. ***Varies.***

BRAIN

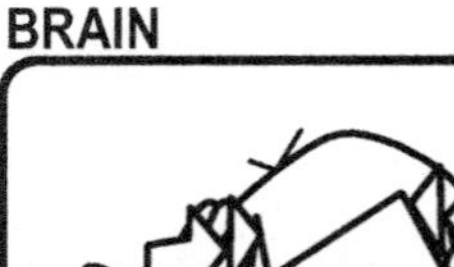

Flat hands tap the head twice. Alternative version is index finger tapping side of head which also means **THINK, SENSIBLE**.

BRANCH

L. open hand held with fingers pointing up; R. full 'C' hand moves in outward arc away from L.

BREAD, LOAF

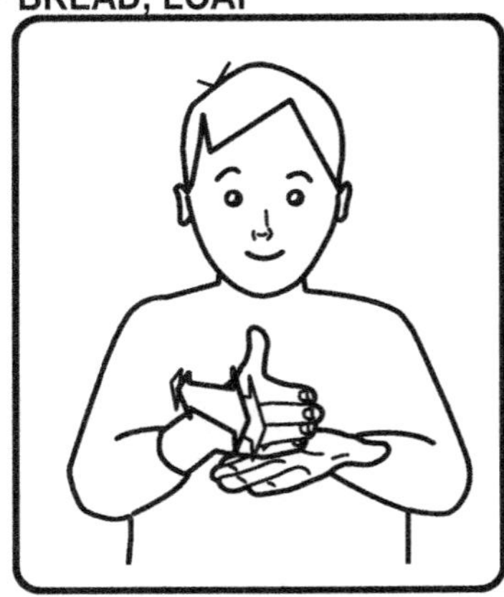

Edge of R. flat hand rubs backwards and forwards on L. palm in sawing action.
May vary.

BREAK, FRACTURE, SNAP

Fists held together twist apart in snapping action.

BREATHE

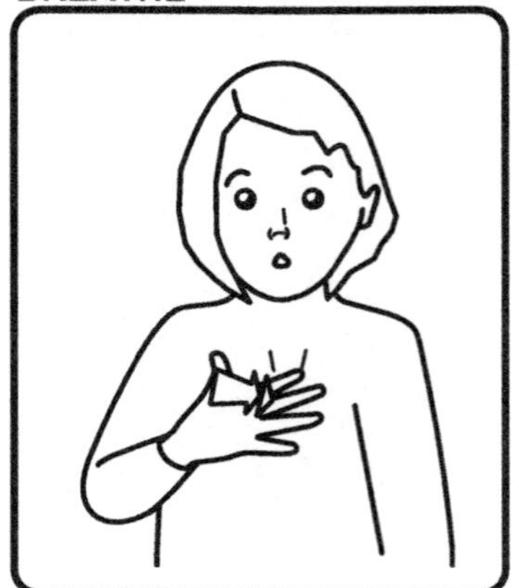

Open hand touches chest in repeated movement to indicate the rise and fall of the chest when breathing.

BRIEF, ABBREVIATE

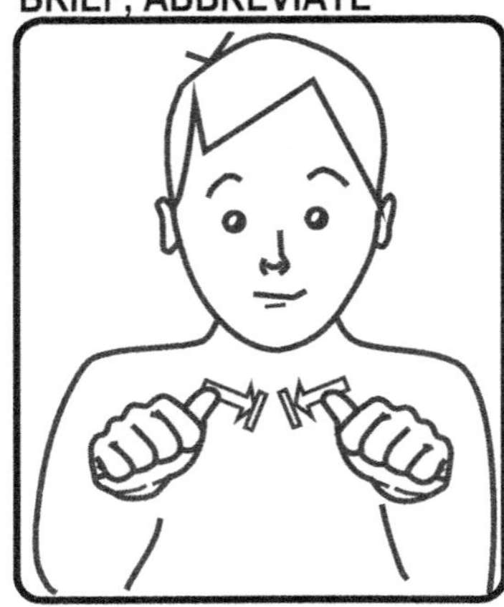

Closed hands with thumbs out make short abrupt movement towards each other. Also means **MINIMUM, SHORT.**

BRIGHT

Palm forward (or palm back) full 'O' hands start together and spring open and apart in upward direction.

BRITTLE

(Easily broken) Irish 'T' hands twist down/apart in repeated snapping movement with slight shrug of shoulders.

BUD

R. thumb and index finger touch tip of L. index finger and open and close in outline shape.

BUD

(Eg. amaryllis) Fingers of clawed hands touch then hands twist apart from wrists in opening movement.

BULB (flower)

R. 'O' hand moves behind L. full 'C' hand and moves upwards, as fingers open.

BULL

Tips of 'O' hand contact the nose.

BUNSEN BURNER

Fingerspell 'B' twice then R. index finger flicks upwards off thumb several times to represent the flame, lips tightly rounded.

BUSH, SHRUB

Palm forward (or palm facing) clawed hands move apart in bushy outline shape.

BUTTERFLY, MOTH

Hands are crossed with thumbs interlocked, and hands bend from knuckles in flapping movements.

CAMOUFLAGE

Palm forward open hands, one in front of the other, move in inward circles.

CAN, COULD, POSSIBLE

Index finger and thumb close together in front of nose. May open and close several times. Also means **POTENTIAL.**

CAN'T, COULDN'T

Index finger moves down and loops over like crossing something out as head shakes. Also **IMPOSSIBLE** (two hands).

CANDLE

Closed hands R. above L. with index and thumbs in narrow 'C' hands; R. hand moves upwards. One of several ***variations.***

CANDLE

Index finger flicks upwards twice off thumb. One of several ***variations.***

CAPACITOR

Fingerspell 'C' then sign **ELECTRICITY** followed by bent hand moving backwards across L. palm (**SAVE**).

CAR, DRIVE, DRIVER

Closed hands move in action of holding and moving a steering wheel. **DRIVE** may be short forward movement of both hands.

CARBON

Fingerspelt initial 'C', or full 'C' hand.

CARBON DAMAGE

Curved hands move round in sphere shape (**WORLD**) then form 'C' (**CARBON**) and open hands twist over against each other (**DAMAGE**).

CARBON DIOXIDE

Fingerspell 'C' 'D'.

CARBON DIOXIDE, CO_2

Fingerspell 'C' 'O' followed by **2**, slightly lower to represent the symbol.

CARD

Palm facing 'O' hands shake backwards and forwards several times. Irish 'T' hands can also be used.

CARE FOR, LOOK AFTER

'V' hands one on top of the other move forward/down together from near eyes. Also means **PROTECT.**

CAREFUL, TAKE CARE

'C' hands move forward/down from near eyes. Index fingers may start straight and flex as they move.

CARNIVORE

(Flesh eating) Index finger prods into neck (**MEAT**) then bunched hand makes two short movements towards the mouth (**EAT**).

CAT, WHISKERS

Fingers flex as hands make short repeated outward movements from sides of mouth. ***Varies.***

CATALYST

(Substance that speeds chemical reaction without itself changing) Fingerspell 'C' then R. index bounces up twice off L. (**FAST**).

CATERPILLAR

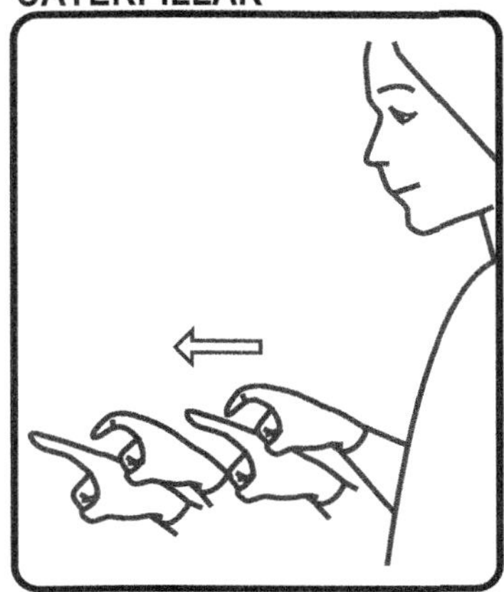

Index finger moves forward flexing repeatedly.

CATHODE

(Negative electrode in electrolysis) R. index held across L. palm (**NEGATIVE**), spell 'C' then indexes point down (**ELECTRODE**).

CELL WALL

L. 'O' hand represents the cell and R. index finger moves round it in circular movement to represent the wall.

CELL, CELLS

R. index finger traces shape in circular movement/s on L. palm or fingerspell.

CELL, CELLS

Palm forward 'O' hand moves around and makes several short forward movements.

CENTRE, MIDDLE

Tip of R. middle finger taps twice into centre of L. palm.

CENTRIPETAL

(Force that keeps objects moving in circle) R. index makes a circle (**CIRCLE**) then changes to flat hand pressing down on L. fist (**FORCE**).

CERAMICS

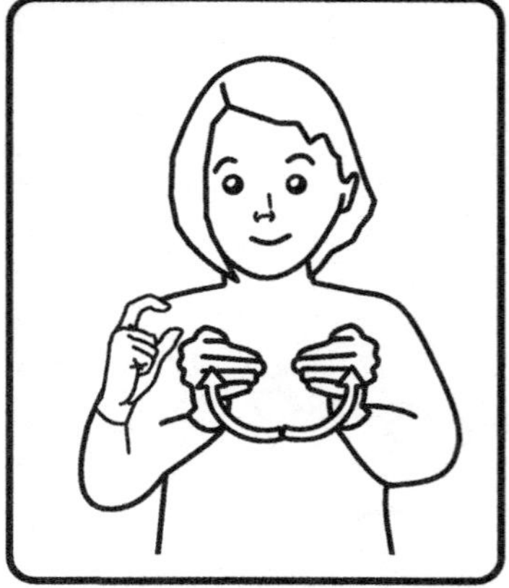

Fingerspell 'C' then bent hands make action of shaping a bowl in clay.

CHANGE, ADAPT, BECOME

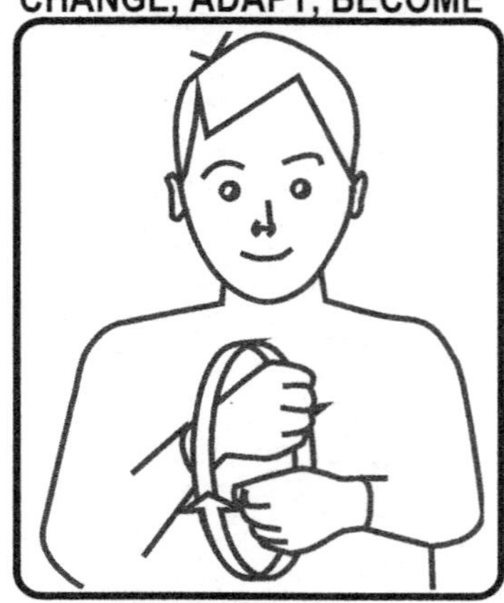

Closed hands circle backwards round each other. ***Varies.***

CHANGE, ALTER, CONVERT

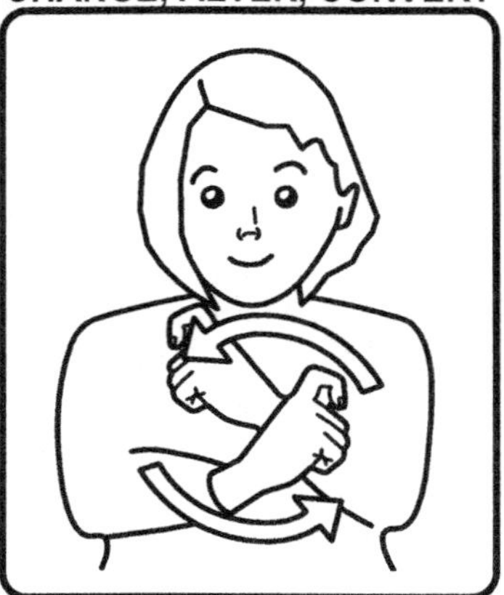

Irish 'T' hands move to cross over each other. Handshape may vary eg. extended index fingers may also be used. ***Varies.***

CHARACTER/ISTIC

Closed hand lands on L. palm and twists to palm forward or in direction of referent. Also means **BELONG TO, CULTURE.**

CHARGE

(Build up of static charge) Index finger zigzags down then open hands move apart in several small arcs (**EXPAND, INCREASE**).

CHARGE

(Eg. battery) R. fist moves up sharply to hit L. palm. Also means **FULL, MAXIMUM, UP TO.**

CHECK, TEST, TRY OUT

Index moves down from eye, then 'Y' hands (or just one hand) move down waggling from the wrists. ***Directional.***

CHEESE

Fingertips of R. bent hand rest on L. palm as R. hand twists repeatedly from the wrist.

CHEMICAL, CHEMIST

Extended R. little finger makes small circular movements in L. full 'C' hand. Also means **MEDICINE, POISON, TOXIC.**

CHEMISTRY

Fingerspell 'C' 'H' then full 'C' hands tip inwards alternately (**SCIENCE**).

CHEW, CHEW UP

R. closed hand rubs in anticlockwise circles on top of L. as jaw makes chewing movements, lips closed.

CHILD, TODDLER

Palm down flat hand makes short movement down. Also means **LOW, SOUTH.**

CHROMATOGRAPHY

'C' hand moves in small circles (**COLOUR**) then palm down open hands move forward/apart (**SPREAD**).

CHROMOSOME

R. index finger makes circle on L. palm (**CELL**) then index traces a wavy line downwards (*inside cell).*

CIRCUIT

R. index finger traces a circle then 'O' hands join together.

CIRCUIT BULB

All the fingers of palm up hand flick open several times in relevant location.

CIRCULATE, CIRCULATION

Index traces circular movements in appropriate location. Illustration indicates *blood circulation*. The sign ***BLOOD*** may be added.

CLASS/IFICATION

Palm facing full 'C' hands twist in to touch finger tips and repeat to the side. Also means **GROUP, COMMUNITY** (of plants/animals).

CLAY

Cupped hands press together then twist over and repeat like shaping ball of clay.

CLIMATE

Hands fan backwards near face (**WEATHER**) then R. bent hand moves from shoulder to touch L. palm (**SINCE, OVER A LONG TIME**).

CLIMATE CHANGE

Hands fan towards face (**WEATHER**) then Irish 'T' hands move slowly round from right shoulder, twisting to change places (**CHANGE**).

CLONE

R. bent hand fingers close onto thumb as it moves away from L. index finger (**COPY**) changing to closed hand with index extended.

CLOUD, CLOUDY

Palm forward clawed hands make repeated alternate circling movements at head height.

COCOON

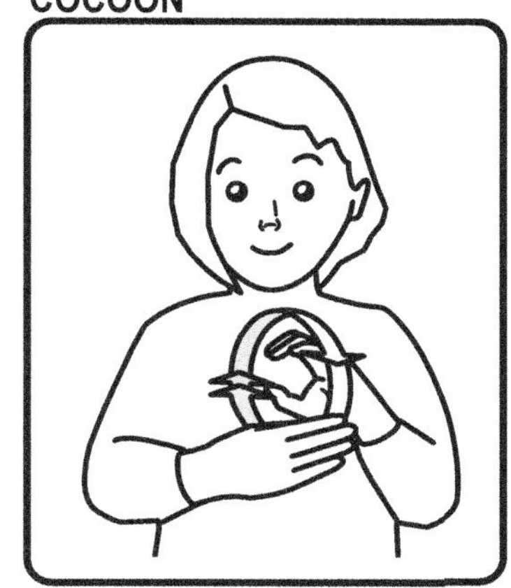

R. palm back flat hand moves in forward circles round L. full 'C' hand several times.

COIL

Index finger moves in outline shape of a coil.

COLD, FREEZING, WINTER

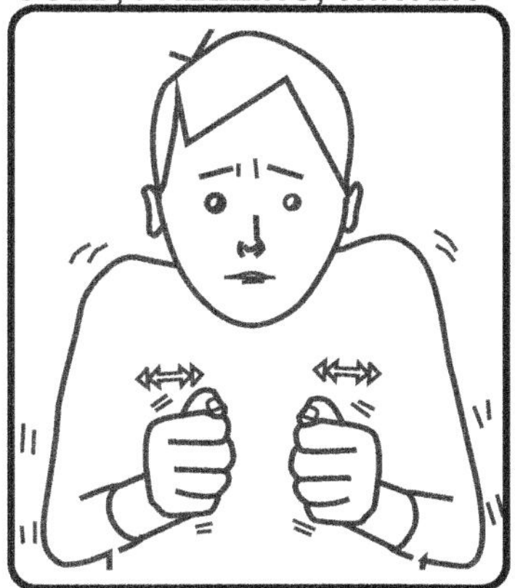

Closed hands and elbows pull into body in shivering action, shoulders hunched, cheeks puffed.

COLLATE, GATHER

Palm forward R. hand moves onto L. palm closing to bunched hand several times as both hands move round to the left.

COLLECT, COLLECTION

R. bent hand brushes backwards across L. palm several times as hands move round in arc to the left. May ***vary.***

COLOUR

'C' hand makes anticlockwise circular movements. Can also be signed with a palm forward open hand. ***Varies.***

COMMUNITY

(Eg. of people) R. 'C' hand (or palm down open hand) sweeps round L. index finger from behind.

COMPARE, COMPARISON

Palm up flat hands move up and down alternately several times. Also means **EVALUATE, JUDGE.**

COMPOUND

Hands held palm facing move in to contact as they close to bunched hands.

CONCAVE

L. full 'C' hand held palm right; R. index finger pointing forward brushes down in inward curve of L. hand.

CONCENTRATED

Palm up fists move in firm outward circular movement with stress, lips pressed together. Also means **CONCENTRATION.**

CONCLUDE, CONCLUSION

Open hands held apart one above the other, come together, fingers closing to full 'O' hands.

CONDENSATION

Open hands held above the head move slowly downwards with fingers wiggling. ***Directional.***

CONDUCTION

Palm back 'C' hand moves forward from nose, closing (**CAN**) then R. flat hand passes through fingers of L. (**THROUGH**) as head nods.

CONNECT/ION, JOIN, LINK

Hands move towards each other and link fingers of 'O' hands. Also means **CONTACT.**

CONSERVATION

'V' hands one on top of the other move down together from near eyes (**CARE FOR**); hands move back to body, R. bent hand on L. palm (**SAVE**).

CONTAMINATED

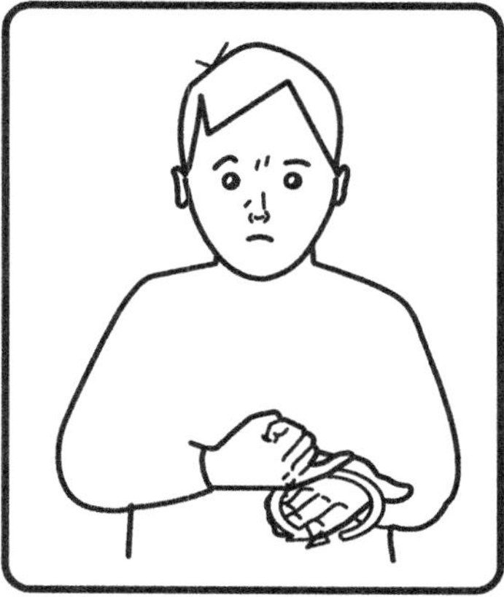

(By undesirable elements) Edge of R. little finger rubs in circles on L. palm with negative expression. Also means **CONTAMINATION.**

CONTINUE, CARRY ON

Palm down 'C' hands (or just one hand) move smoothly to the right, or forwards. Also means **PERMANENT.**

CONTRACT, REDUCE

(Eg. metal) Palm facing 'N' (or flat) hands make short movement in/down towards each other. Also means **DECREASE, LESS, SHORT.**

CONTRACT/ION

(Reduce length or volume) Clawed hands move towards each other with emphasis, cheeks puffed. Also means **COMPRESS/ION, SQUASH.**

CONTRACT/ION

(Eg. muscle) Open hand on arm (or relevant part of body) contracts to a clawed hand, or open hands on abdomen move towards each other.

CONTROL, MANAGE

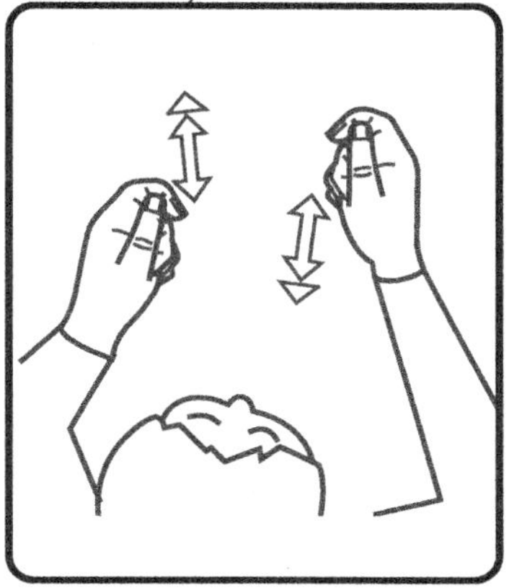

Palm facing Irish 'T' hands move alternately backwards and forwards. Also means **ADMINISTER, DEAL WITH, RUN.**

CONVECTION

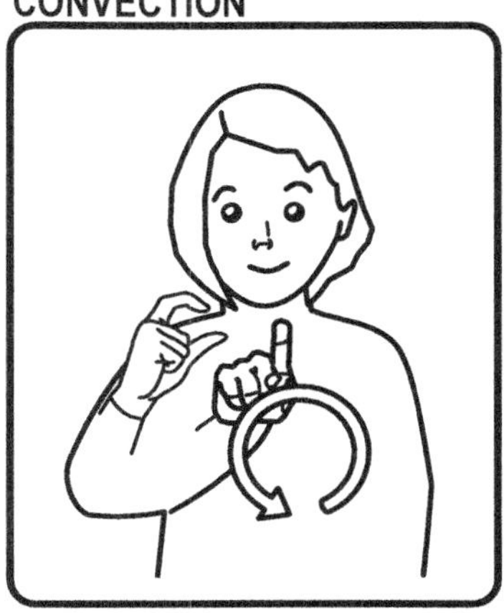

(Spreading or moving heat through a liquid or gas) Fingerspell 'C' then index finger (or flat hand) moves round in circle.

CONVEX

L. full 'C' hand held palm right; R. index finger pointing forward draws an outward curve away from L. hand.

COOK/ER, FRY, PAN

Palm up Irish 'T' hand makes repeated forward shaking movements. Also means **FEED (*directional*).**

COOL

Hands fan backwards towards the cheeks several times, the lips are rounded.

CORROSION, RUST

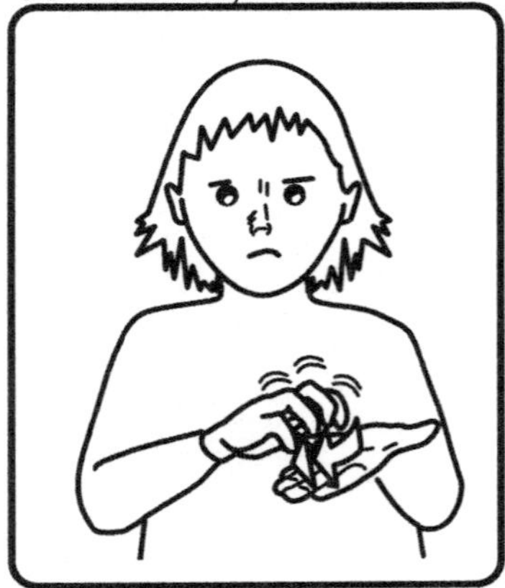

R. clawed hand makes crawling or scraping movements on L. hand, with negative facial expression.

COUNTRYSIDE, HILLS

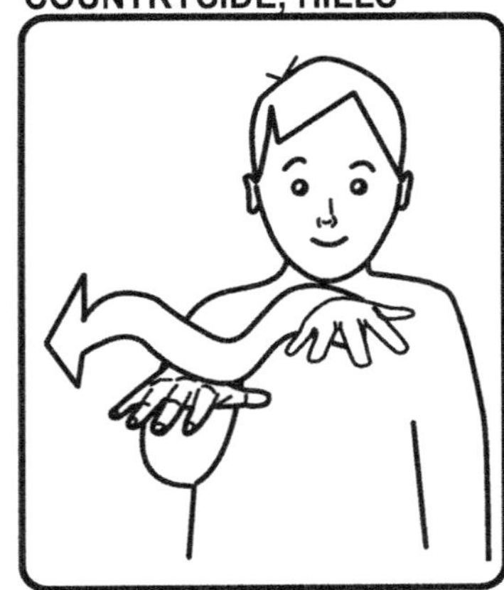

Palm down hand moves up and down several times in wavy movement to the right. Single large movement gives one version of **MOUNTAIN.**

COW

Thumb tips of 'Y' hands touch sides of head and twist upwards from palm down to palm forward.

CRYSTAL

Fingerspell 'C' then fingers of palm up clawed hand wiggle.

CURRENT

'C' hand (or index finger) moves sideways in a wavy movement.

CYCLE

Index finger makes repeated large circular movements in the air.

DAMAGE, DESTROY

Heels of open hands contact R. on top of L. then twist over firmly from wrists to change places L. on R. Also means **SPOIL, WRECK.**

DANGER/OUS, HAZARD

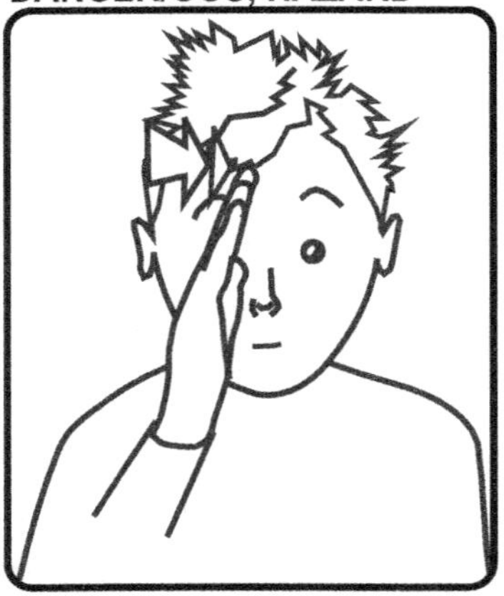

Edge of R. flat hand comes up sharply to forehead. May tap twice on forehead.

DARK, EVENING, NIGHT

Palm back hands swing in/down to finish crossed. Also means **DARKNESS.**

DAY, DAWN, LIGHT

Palm back open hands start crossed and swing upwards and apart. **DAY** is often also fingerspelt.

DEAD, DEATH, DIE, DYING

'N' hands held apart and pointing forward twist down abruptly from wrists. Slow movement for **DYING.**

DECAY

With negative facial expression, thumbs rub across fingertips of palm up hands.

DEEP, DEPTH

R. 'L' hand moves down behind palm down L. hand. Puffed cheeks to indicate great depth.

DEFLATE, FLATTEN

R. flat hand moves down onto L. palm, or similar to suit context.

DEGREES C

Touch index fingertip and thumb to form 'O' hand then form fingerspelt 'C'.

DENSITY

Fingerspell 'D' then bring clawed hands together. Puffed cheeks to indicate high density.

DEVELOP, DEVELOPMENT

R. bunched hand twists upwards in clockwise movement as all fingers spread open behind L. flat hand.

DIAGRAM

Index fingers trace outline shape.

DIAPHRAGM

Flat hand is drawn left to right in upward curve across the stomach below the ribs.

DIFFERENT, DIFFERENCE

Index fingers held together twist over and apart.

DIFFRACTION

(The breaking up or spreading of waves) Palm down hands move forward/apart in wavy movements.

DIFFUSE, DIFFUSION

Fingerspell 'D' then palm down open hands move forward/apart (**SPREAD**) with fingers wiggling.

DIFFUSE, DIFFUSION

(Eg. through a membrane or filter paper) Fingerspell 'D' then R. hand fingers wiggle through fingers of L. hand (**FILTER**).

DIGEST, DIGESTION

Bunched hand to mouth (**FOOD**) then index traces path to stomach and closed hands, one on top of the other, grind together.

DIGITAL

Fingerspell 'D' then R. hand moves to the right opening and closing index and thumb several times in quick movement.

DILUTE, DILUTION

(To make less concentrated) Fingerspell 'D' then R. hand little finger brushes down upper left arm (**WEAK**).

DINOSAUR

Clawed hands move slowly and deliberately in alternate stepping movements with shoulders hunched.

DIODE

(Allows current to flow one way only) Fingers of R. hand pass through L. with headnod (**THROUGH**), then twist back with headshake.

DIPLOID

(Full number of chromosomes in a cell) Closed hand taps chin twice (**NUMBER**) then R. bent hand moves up under L. (**FULL**).

DISAPPEAR, VANISH

Open hands with fingers angled towards each other pull apart snapping closed to bunched hands as open mouth closes.

DISEASE, ILLNESS

Extended little fingers brush twice down chest with negative facial expression.

DISPERSAL

(Eg. wind dispersal) Fingers of R. hand wiggle as hand moves to the right away from L. upright index finger.

DISPLACE

Clawed hand moves to the side as fingers spring open.

DISSOLVE

Palm up bunched hands start together then move apart as thumbs rub across fingertips from little finger to thumb.

DISTANCE

Index fingers start together then R. hand moves away in large forward arc.

DISTIL, DISTILLATION

Fingers of palm up hands wiggle as hands move up above head (**EVAPORATE**) then twist over and move down wiggling (**CONDENSE**).

DIVIDE, SPLIT, SHARE

(Eg. binary fission - cell divides to produce new cells) Blade of R. hand lands on L. palm, twists and repeats. Also means **RATIO.**

DOLPHIN

R. bent hand bends at the wrist to make up and down wavy movements as it moves to the left. ***Varies.***

DOMINANT

Palm up fists move up/back with emphasis. Also means **STRONG, STRENGTH.**

DOWN, SOUTH

Index finger points down and makes small downward movement. Also means **THIS, HERE, DOWNSTAIRS** (may repeat).

DRINK

Full 'C' hand moves to mouth with small backward tipping movement. Also used for **WATER.**

DRY, DRY UP, DRIED

Thumbs rub across the pads of the fingers from little fingers to indexes. One hand can be used.

DRY, THIRST, THIRSTY

Finger and thumb tips grasp throat and pull down, closing to bunched hand. Tongue slightly protrudes. Also means **ARID.**

DUCK, GOOSE

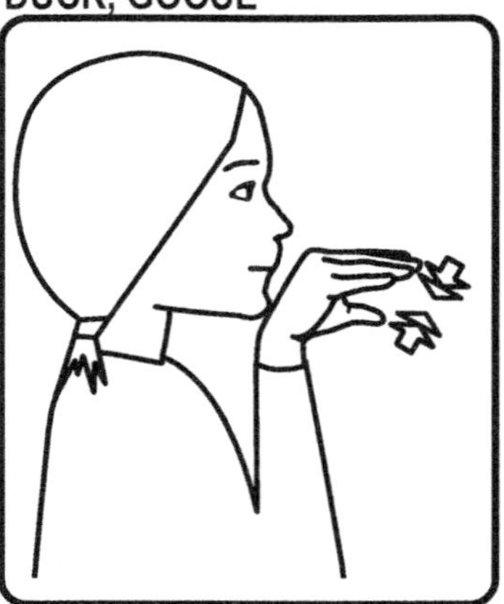

Fingers of bent hand (or 'N' hand) open and close onto thumb several times in front of chin.

EAR

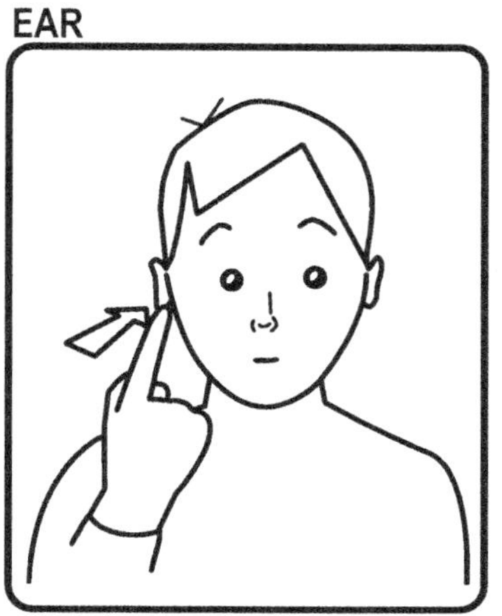

Index finger points to ear.

EARTHQUAKE, TREMOR

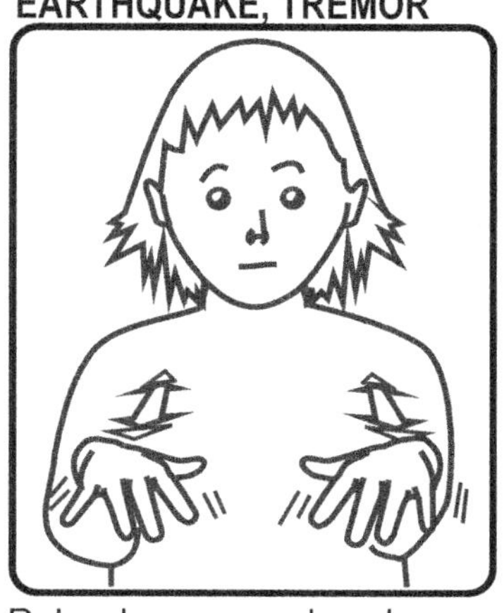

Palm down open hands shake repeatedly backwards and forwards simultaneously.

EAST

R. flat hand with fingers pointing up, makes small movement to the right.

EAT, FOOD

Bunched hand makes two short movements to the mouth. Also used for **CONSUME, CONSUMER.**

ECOSYSTEM

Interlinked 'O hands move round in large circle followed by extended thumb twisting from wrist moving round in large circle.

EFFORT, WORK

Blade of R. flat hand makes forward chopping moving at right angles against edge of L. flat hand. Also means **PRACTICAL.**

EGG, OVUM

Fingerspell 'E' 'G' 'G' or form an 'O' or full 'O' hand.

ELASTIC, STRETCH

Fists pull apart in stretching movement. Also means **PULL OUT.** Repeat for **ELASTICITY.**

ELASTIC/ITY, STRETCHY

Palm up bent 'V' hands pull apart with repeated movement. Handshape may ***vary.***

ELBOW

Index finger taps left elbow twice.

ELECTRIC CURRENT

Tips of R. bent 'V' hand tap chin twice (**ELECTRIC** ***regional***) then 'C' hand moves left to right in wavy movement.

ELECTRIC CURRENT

Index finger moves down in zigzag (**ELECTRIC** ***regional***) then 'C' hand moves left to right in wavy movement.

ELECTRIC, ELECTRICITY

Thumb tip of palm left R. 'L' hand brushes forward twice from under the chin. ***Regional.***

ELECTRIC, ELECTRICITY

Palm forward index finger moves down in zigzag movement. ***Regional.***

ELECTRICAL CONDUCTION

Sign **ELECTRIC** then 'C' hand moves forward from nose, closing as head nods and R. flat hand passes through fingers of L.

ELECTRICAL INSULATION

Sign **ELECTRIC** then R. flat hand passes through fingers of L. as head shakes.

ELECTRODES

Both index fingers point and make a short movement down simultaneously.

ELECTROLYSIS

Sign **ELECTRICITY** then index fingers point and make a short movement down simultaneously (**ELECTRODES**).

ELECTROLYSIS

Sign **ELECTRICITY** then index fingers point and make a short movement down simultaneously (**ELECTRODES**).

ELECTROMAGNET/IC

Sign **ELECTRICITY** then index fingers point and make a short movement to contact each other with cheeks sucked in (**MAGNET**).

ELECTROMAGNET/IC

Sign **ELECTRICITY** then index fingers point and make a short movement to contact each other with cheeks sucked in (**MAGNET**).

ELECTRON

Fingerspell 'E' then R. index held across L. palm taps twice (**NEGATIVE**) and index makes small circles (electrons round an orbit).

ELECTRONICS

Sign **ELECTRICITY** then 'N' hands with thumbs closed onto them make small movements like placing leads in a circuit.

ELECTRONICS

Sign **ELECTRICITY** then 'N' hands with thumbs closed onto them make small movements like placing leads in a circuit.

ELEMENT

(An element is made of only one kind of atom) Extended R. index finger moves down behind and to the side of L. palm back full 'C' hand.

EMBRYO, FOETUS

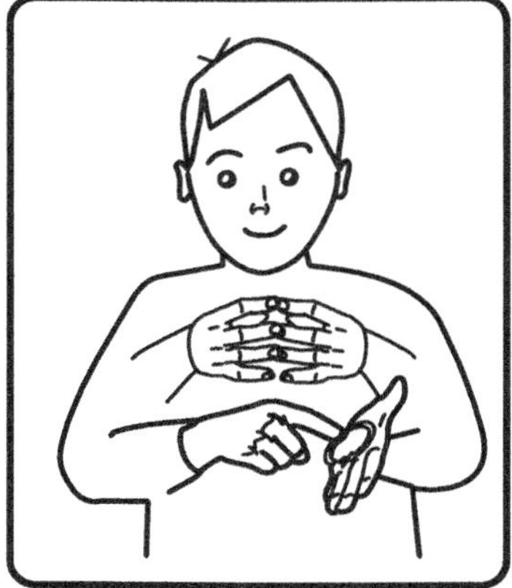

Tips of clawed hands touch (**GROUP**) then index finger moves in small circles on L. palm (**CELLS**).

EMBRYO, FOETUS

Flat hands on abdomen (**WOMB, UTERUS**) then make small movement inwards, shoulders raised (**SMALL**) then arms rock (**BABY**).

EMISSIONS, POLLUTION

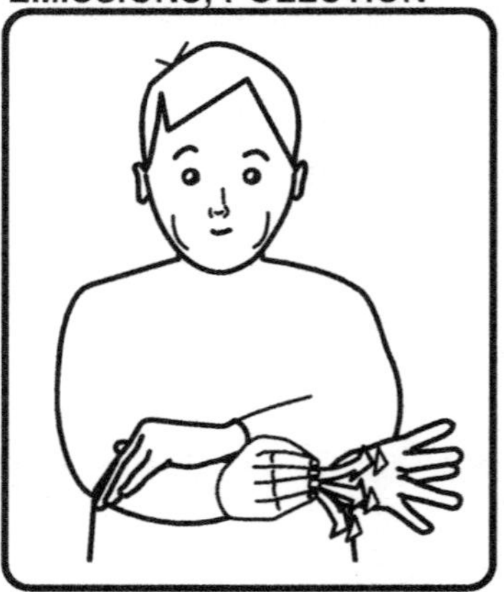

Left arm rests across right as R. bunched hand opens and closes repeatedly to the side, cheeks puffed. Also means **EXHAUST FUMES.**

ENDANGERED, DECREASE

Flat hands (or 'N' hands) held apart move down/in towards each other in several short movements. Also **CONTRACT, DECLINE, REDUCE.**

ENERGY

Fists make two short movements back towards the chest.

ENOUGH, SUFFICIENT

Bent hand brushes upwards/forwards twice under the chin. Also means **PLENTY**.

ENVIRONMENT/AL

Fingers of palm down R. open hand wiggle as hand makes circular movements above upright L. index finger.

ENZYME

(Catalyst that speeds reactions without changing itself) Fingerspell 'E' 'N' 'Z' then R. index bounces up twice of L. (**FAST**).

EQUAL, FAIR

Bent hands touch at tips, then move apart. ***Varies.***

EQUIPMENT

Fingerspell 'E' 'Q', or palm back clawed hands swivel downwards to interlock with each other.

EQUIPMENT, MACHINERY

Palm back clawed hands swing down/in towards each other so that fingers intermesh. Also means **TECHNOLOGY.**

ESTIMATE

Index finger touches side of forehead (**THINK**) then palm down open hand moves in circles (**ABOUT, APPROX.**) lips stretched or pushed forward.

EVAPORATE

Fingers of palm up open hands wiggle as hands move upwards. Also means **EVAPORATION.**

EVOLVE, EVOLUTION

Irish 'T' hands start at right shoulder and slowly move forward/down and cross over each other.

EVOLVE, EVOLUTION

Closed hands circle backwards round each other then R. flat hand moves forward/down from shoulder to contact L. palm.

EXPERIMENT

R. index finger, thumb and little finger extended; index starts near eye then two 'Y' hands move down twisting alternately from wrists.

EXTINCT, EXTINCTION

Palm down R. flat hand sweeps round in horizontal circle, then brushes emphatically along L. palm, lips pressed together.

EYE

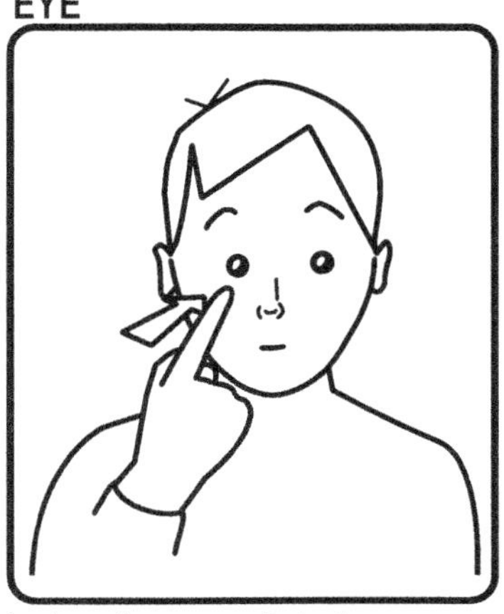

Index finger points to eye.

FACE

Index finger pointing to face moves round it in circular movement.

FACTORY, COMPANY, FIRM

Closed hands with thumbs up start together one behind the other, and move apart diagonally.

FAIR TEST

Palm down flat hands move apart in small arcs (**FAIR**) followed by the sign for **EXPERIMENT, TEST.**

FALLOPIAN TUBES

Fingerspell 'EGG' then trace outline on appropriate part of body with index fingers and thumbs. Also called **EGG TUBES, OVIDUCTS.**

FALSE, FAKE, NOT REAL

Tip of extended middle finger touches nose, then moves and twists to point forward. Also means **ARTIFICIAL, PRETEND.**

FAMILY

Open hand (or fingerspelt 'F') moves round in horizontal circles. This version also means **ABOUT, AREA, APPROXIMATELY.**

FARM, FARMER

Palm down closed hand with thumb out moves from chest in forward arc to recontact the body. Also means **AGRICULTURE.**

FAT, LARGE, OBESE

Palm back open hands move forward/apart with emphasis as cheeks puff out. Also signed with palm down closed hands, thumbs out.

FAUNA, WILDLIFE

(All the animals of a region) Sign **ANIMAL** then R. index finger brushes repeatedly against L. as they move sideways (**ALL KINDS OF**).

FEATHER/S

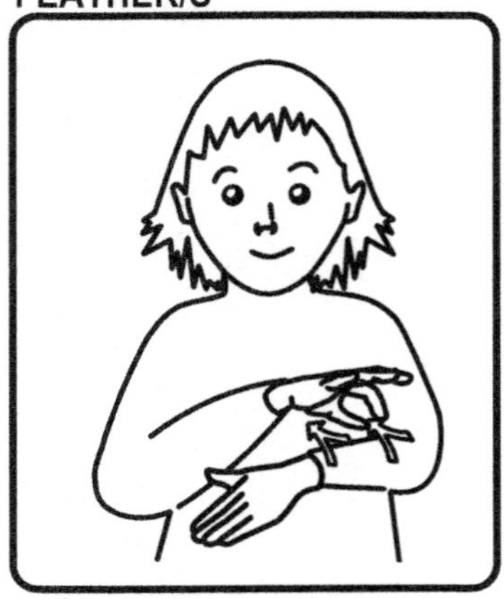

R. index finger and thumb make repeated closing, plucking movements on left arm.

FEED, COOK, TREAT

Irish 'T' hands make short movements forward or towards referent. ***Directional.***

FEEL, FEELINGS, EMOTION

Tips of middle fingers brush upwards on chest. One hand can be used.

FEET

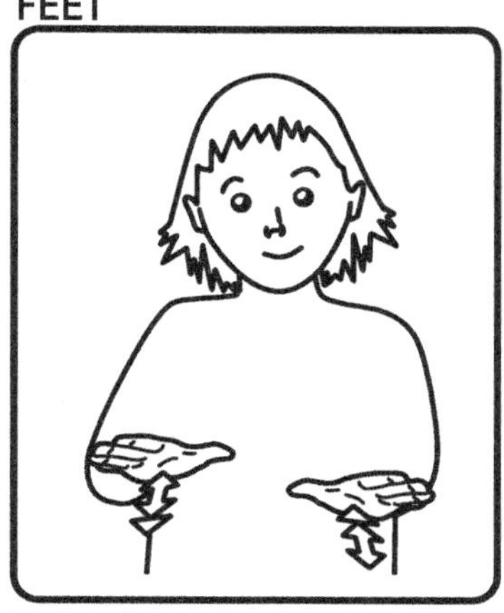

Palm down flat hands move up and down alternately several times. May move forward **(STEPS, WALK).**

FEET

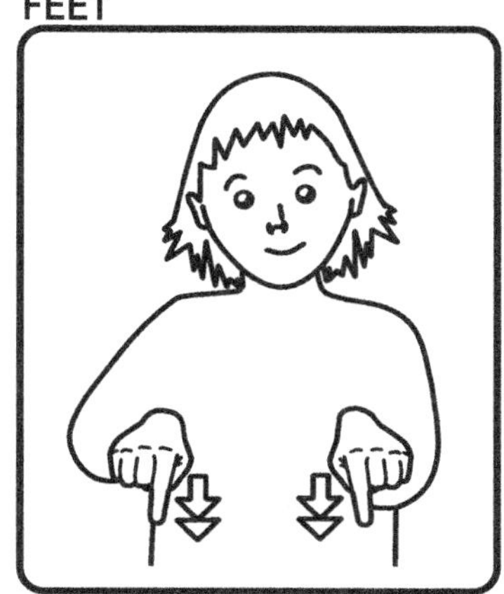

Index fingers pointing down make two short downward movements. One hand and movement for **FOOT.**

FEMALE, WOMAN, GIRL

Palm forward index finger brushes forward twice across cheek. ***Varies.***

FERMENT/ATION

Palm up full 'O' hands make small repeated upward and opening movements alternately.

FERTILISATION

R. index finger wriggles forward (**SPERM**) towards L. 'O' hand (**EGG**) then 'O' hands interlock (**JOIN**).

FIBRE

(Structure or material composed of fibres) 'O' hands in contact pull apart and repeat several times moving down.

FIBRE, THREAD

Palm up 'O' hands pull apart as the thumbs rub across the index fingertips.

FIELD, GRASS, GREEN

R. flat hand sweeps up left forearm. **Colours can vary widely.**

FILTER

Wiggling fingers of R. hand pass through fingers of L. ***Directional.***

FILTER

(Eg. through a funnel) Fingers of R. hand close together into a bunched hand in repeated movement down behind L. full 'C' hand.

FIND, DISCOVER

Index points to eye, then moves away closing sharply to a fist in upward grasping movement.

FINISH, END, STOP

Fingers of bent hands close onto thumbs in short firm downward movement. Also means **CONCLUDE, TERMINATE.**

FIRE, BURN, FLAMES

Fingers of palm facing open hands wiggle as hands move up and down alternately. May ***vary in context.***

FIREWORKS

Palm forward index fingers move upwards and outwards alternately several times.

FISH

Flat hand moves diagonally forward with quick waggling movements from the wrist.

FISSION

(Eg. nuclear fission, nucleus of atom splits to release energy) Closed hands together pull apart with force, cheeks puffed.

FISSURE, CRACK

Index finger moves in jagged line to indicate a crack or fissure eg. in rocks.

FLEXIBLE

Irish 'T' hands flex forward and back from wrists several times. Bunched hands may also be used.

FLOOD, RISING WATER

Palm down open hands move up simultaneously. Cheeks may be puffed.

FLORA

(All the plants of a region) Sign **FLOWER** then R. index finger brushes repeatedly against L. as they move sideways (**ALL KINDS OF**).

FLOWER

'O' hand (or bunched or Irish 'T' hand) moves from side to side under the nose as if sniffing a flower. Also **GARDEN** (***regional***).

FOOD CHAIN

Bunched hand moves to mouth (**FOOD**) then extended thumb twists repeatedly from wrist moving round in big circle.

FORCE

R. flat hand pushes down (or sideways) against L. fist with pressure, lips stretched. ***Directional.***

FOREST, WOODS

Upright R. open hand twists from the wrist, elbow on L. palm, as the formation sweeps round to the left.

FOX

Palm back bent hand with thumb pointing back moves forward sharply from the nose closing to a bunched hand.

FREQUENCY, PITCH

Index finger moves sideways in wavy line. Quick repeated movements for **HIGH FREQUENCY** and slower for **LOW FREQUENCY**.

FREQUENT, FREQUENCE

Palm left R. 'V' hand makes repeated downward shaking movements as it moves sideways. Also one version of **REPRODUCE.**

FRICTION

Hands form fingerspelt 'F' formation and extended fingers of both hands rub together.

FROG

Fingers of R. 'V' hand flex in hopping movements up left arm or full 'C' hand moves forward from neck. ***Varies.***

FROZEN, ICE, ICY

Palm down open hands move back to body, as fingers curve to form clawed hands. Also means **FREEZE, FREEZING POINT**.

FRUIT

Fingers waggle as R. hand moves from right to left under the chin. One of several ***variations.*** Also one version of **LIQUID, WATER.**

FUEL

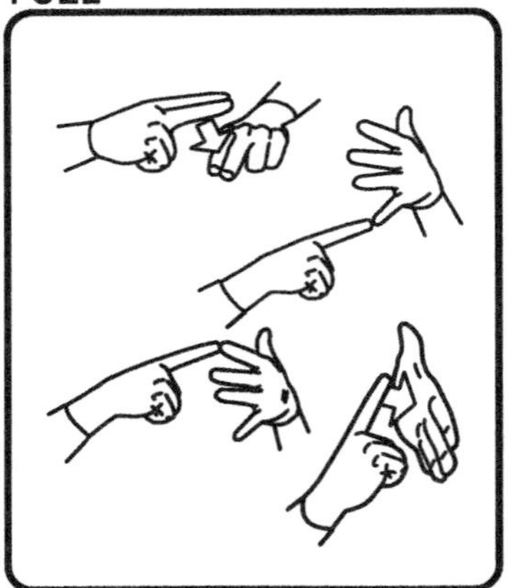

(A material that is a source of thermal energy (heat) eg. petrol, coal, gas, wood) Fingerspell 'F' 'U' 'E' 'L'.

FUEL (thermal energy)

Palm back clawed hand is drawn across the mouth (**HEAT**) then 'C' hand moves forward closing near face (**CAN**) as head nods.

FULCRUM, PIVOT

R. 'O' hand touches tip of L. index finger and twists forwards from the wrist.

FULL, FULL UP, FILL

R. bent hand moves up to contact underside of L. bent hand. Also means **UP TO, MAXIMUM.** May ***vary.***

FUNNEL

Index fingers outline shape of a funnel.

FUR

Tips of open hands on body move forward several times closing to bunched hands.

FUSE

Palm forward closed hand with index and thumb extended and bent to indicate small fuse, moves forward.

FUSE

Fingerspell 'F' then index and thumbs move apart and close in outline shape.

FUSION

Fingerspell 'F' then 'O' hands link together (**JOIN**).

FUTURE, AHEAD

R. flat hand contacts edge of L. hand and moves in large forward arc.

GAMETE

Fingerspell 'G' then index and little fingers contact (**SEX**) and R. index makes small circle on L. palm (**CELLS**).

GARDEN, DIG

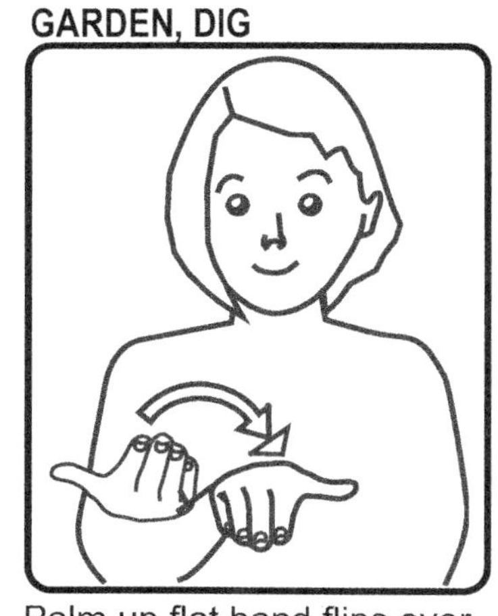

Palm up flat hand flips over to palm down several times. ***Varies.***

GAS

Fingerspell 'G' then hands make circular fanning movements near the sides of the head (**AIR**).

GAS

Fingerspell 'G' 'A' 'S'.

GAUZE

Fingerspell 'G' then lay R. open hand palm down on top of L.

GENE

Fingertips of 'O' hands touch then hands twist and move slightly apart.

GENERAL, COMMON

Palm down flat hands held together move in wide horizontal circle. Also means **CONSISTENT.**

GENERATION

Closed hands with thumbs out rotate round each other moving forward/down from right shoulder. Also one version of **HEREDITARY.**

GENETICS, CHROMOSOME

'V' hands touch at tips, R. palm forward and L. palm back; hands pull apart and twist to finish R. palm back and L. forward.

GENOTYPE

(The genes on a chromosome) Sign **GENE** then **CHROMOSOME**.

GEOGRAPHY

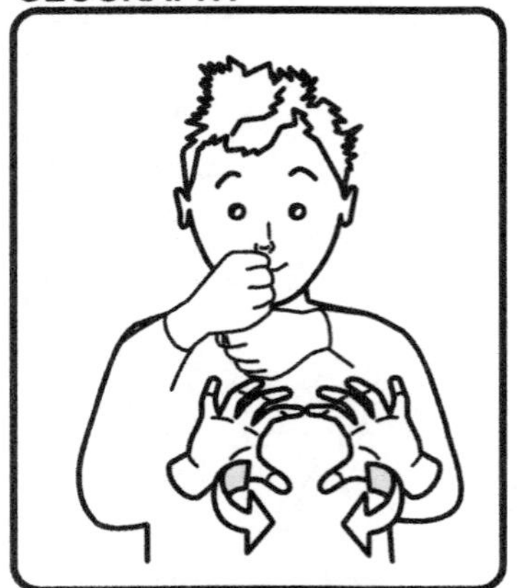

Fingerspell 'G' followed by curved hands moving apart and down in spherical shape (**EARTH**).

GERM

Fingerspell 'G' then palm down open hands move forward/apart, fingers wiggling (**SPREAD**).

GLASS

Palm up open hand makes twisting movements from wrist or flicks middle finger off thumb several times. ***Regional.***

GLASS

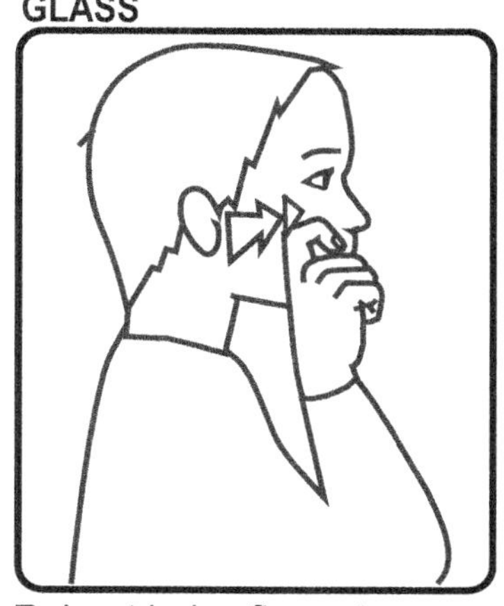

R. bent index finger taps upper cheek twice, or tip of bent index finger taps chin. ***Regional.***

GLOBAL WARMING

Palm forward open hands, fingers curved moves round in outline sphere shape, then R. index moves up behind L. upright index finger.

GOGGLES

Full 'C' hands tap twice at sides of eyes. Also means **SAFETY GLASSES.**

GOLD, GOLDEN

Hands form fingerspelt 'G' then spring open and apart.

GRAPH POINTS

(Plot points on a graph) L 'L' hand held forward; R. index finger makes several short forward jabs to the right to represent points on a graph.

GRASS, VEGETATION

Fingers of R. hand wiggle as they move along behind left forearm.

GRAVITY

Palm up clawed hands move down closing firmly with stress.

GRAVITY

Hands in fingerspelt 'G' formation make short firm movement down.

GROUND, LAND

(Solid surface of the earth) Palm down flat hands held together in front of waist pull apart. Also means **FLOOR.**

GROUP, TYPE

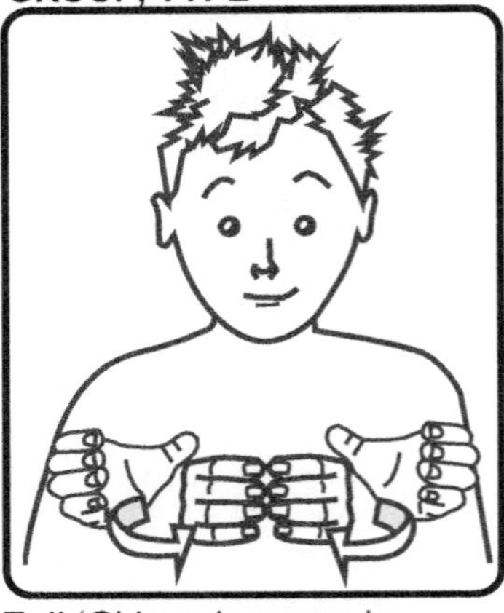

Full 'C' hands move in twisting at the wrists to touch together at fingertips. ***Varies***.

GROW UP, GROW

(Eg. human growth) Palm down flat hand moves upwards.

GROW, BLOOM, DEVELOP

(Eg. plant growth) R. full 'O' hand moves up as fingers spread open behind palm back L. full 'C' hand. Also means **SPRING**.

HABITAT

Palm forward 'C' hands make firm movement forward/down (**STAY**), then palm up open hand makes circles (**WHERE**).

HABITAT, NATIVE

Middle fingertip rubs side of chest (**LIVE**), palm down hand moves in circles (**AREA**) and closed hand moves towards referent (**BELONG**).

HAIR

Fingertips of 'O' hand touch the head as hand makes quick twisting movements from wrist, or Irish 'T' hand makes tugging movements.

HAPLOID

(Half number of chromosomes in cell) R. flat hand slices backwards off L. palm (**HALF**) then closed hand taps chin (**NUMBER**).

HARD, DIFFICULT/Y

Tip of R. thumb prods into L. palm twice, eyebrows furrowed.

HARD, FIRM

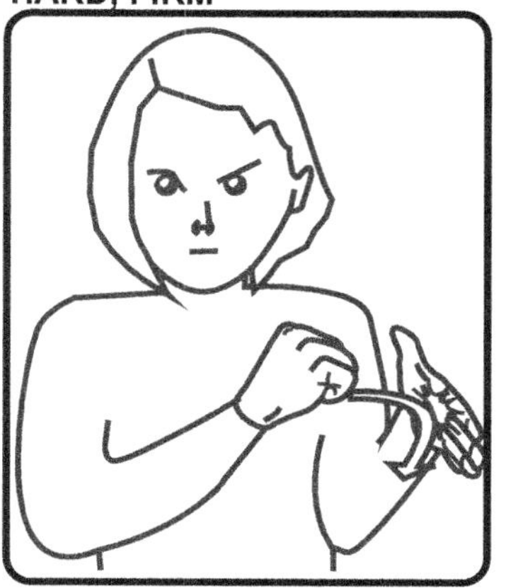

Knuckles of R. closed hand strike firmly downwards across L. palm, eyes narrowed.

HAZE, FOG, MIST

Palm forward open hands move down and cross over in front of face, eyes slightly squinted.

HEAD

Tips of flat hand tap side of head twice.

HEALTH AND SAFETY

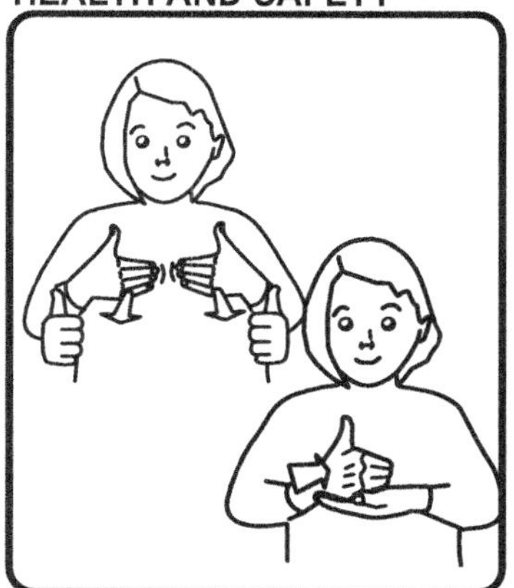

Tips of flat hands touch chest, and move forward, thumbs up, then edge of R. bent hand rests on L. palm as hands move back.

HEAR, HEARING, LISTEN

(The sense of hearing) Slightly cupped hand placed behind the ear. The head may be slightly turned.

HEART

Flat hand taps left side of chest twice.

HEART

Index fingers form outline shape over the heart.

HEAT PROOF (eg. mat)

Clawed hand moves sharply across mouth (**HEAT**) then crossed fists move slightly forward (**PROOF**). Indexes outlining ***MAT*** can be added.

HEAT, HOT

Palm back R. clawed hand is drawn sharply left to right in front of the mouth. Also means **THERMAL.**

HEDGE, BUSHES

Palm forward R. clawed hand moves to the right behind the left arm.

HEDGEHOG

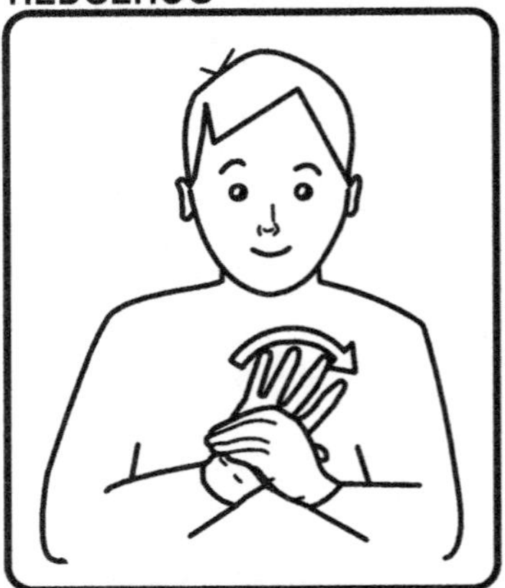

R. palm forward open hand swivels to the left from the wrist, behind L. bunched hand. ***Varies.***

HERBIVORE

(Plant eating animal) R. bunched hand moves up and opens behind L. then R. bunched hand makes two small movements to mouth.

HEREDITARY

Palm back R. bent hand moves forward/down from right should in several small steps to contact palm back L. hand.

HIBERNATION

(Inactive state in which some animals survive winter) Sign **COLD** then open hands pass eyes and snap shut (**SLEEP**).

HOMEOSTASIS

(Keeping body in stable condition) Flat hands move down sides of body then palm down 'C' hands move sideways (**CONTINUE**).

HORMONES

Spell 'H' then open hands one above the other rub in circles on body. Without 'H' also means **EMOTION/AL** (with appropriate expression).

HORSE SHOE MAGNET

Press R. 'C' hand on L. palm and bounce off, cheeks sucked in. Also indicates **MAGNETIC ATTRACTION.**

HOT WEATHER, SWEAT

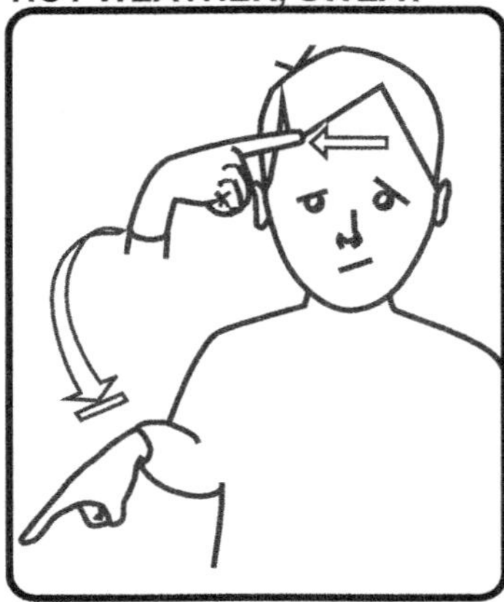

R. index finger (or flat hand) is drawn left to right across forehead, then shakes firmly downwards.

HOT, HEAT, HEATING

Clawed hand is drawn sharply across the mouth. Can be flat hand drawn across forehead then shaken.

HUMAN

(Homo sapiens) Tips of 'C' hand move down centre of body.

HUMANKIND

Palm forward index makes small wavy movement down (**PEOPLE**) then R. index pointing down near L. makes large horizontal circle.

HURRICANE

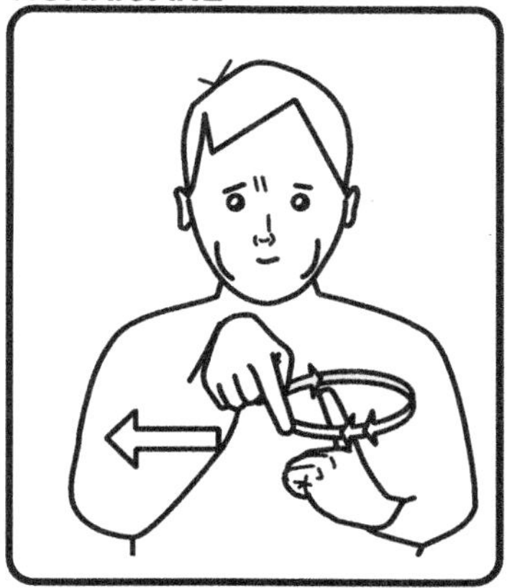

R. Index points down and L. points up as fingers circle quickly round each other moving right.

HYBRID

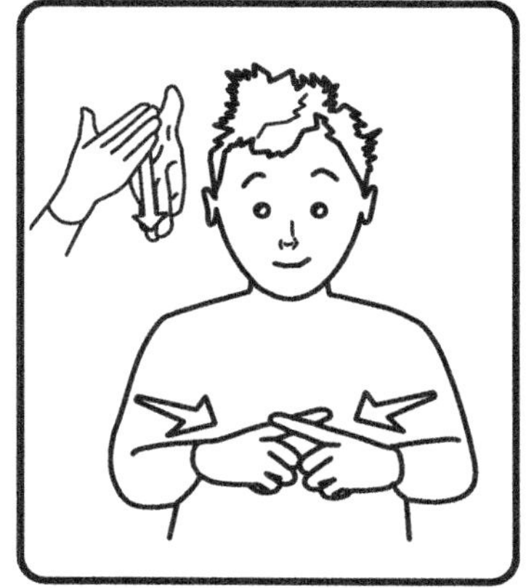

Fingerspell 'H' then index fingers pointing forward/in move towards each other to finish crossed over (**CROSS**).

HYDROELECTRIC

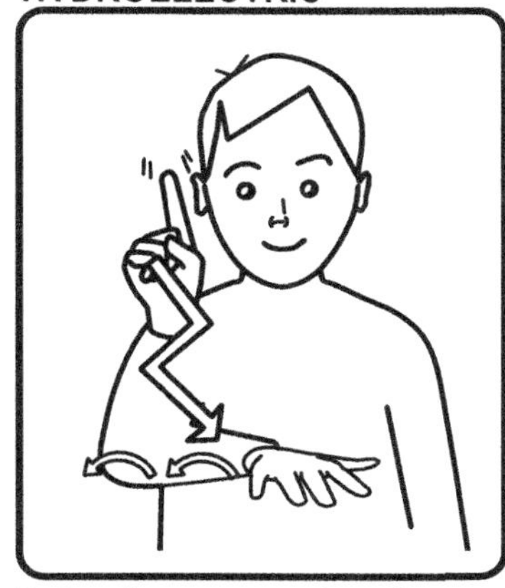

Palm down open hand makes wavy movements to the right (**WATER**) then index finger makes large downward zigzag (**ELECTRICITY**).

HYDROELECTRIC

'O' hand brushes forward on cheek (**WATER**) then index finger makes large downward zigzag (**ELECTRICITY**).

ICE-CREAM, CORNET

Fist makes repeated downward brushing movements near mouth, tongue slightly out.

IMMUNE

Flat hands contact chest, move down and repeat (**BODY**) then R. fist pushes forward against L. index (**PREVENT, DEFEND**).

INDICATOR

Fingerspell 'I' then flat hands move from below eyes, forward/down (**SHOW**).

INERT

Head shakes (**NOT**) as facing clawed hands circle alternately (**REACTIVE**).

INFLATE (eg. BALLOON)

'O' hand is held near mouth then open hands move apart in small arc.

INHERIT, INHERITANCE

Palm back bent hand moves forward/down from shoulder in small arcs towards front of body, then palm up hand moves back to chest.

INHERIT, INHERITANCE

Palm back hands circle round each other forward/down towards front of body.

INJECT, INJECTION, DRUG

Thumb closes onto fingers of 'V' hand in action of syringe on upper arm (or appropriate part of body). Also means **VACCINATE, VACCINE.**

INPUT

R. bunched hand is placed inside L. full 'C' hand.

INSECT

Fingers of palm down hand wiggle as hand moves forward/left. ***Varies.***

INSOLUBLE

Palm up bunched hands move apart as thumbs rub across fingertips and head shakes.

INSTRUCTION

Palm back index fingers move alternately forward/out from the mouth. Also means **INFORMATION**.

INSULATION

(Eg. electrical) Head shakes in negation as R. flat hand passes forward/left through fingers of L. (**THROUGH**)

INTO

Fingers of R. bent hand are tucked into L. full 'C' hand in two movements.

INVERTEBRATE

R. hand taps over shoulder (**BACK**), tight 'C's pull apart (**SPINE**) and flat hand moves sharply across mouth as head shakes (**NOT GOT**).

INVERTEBRATE

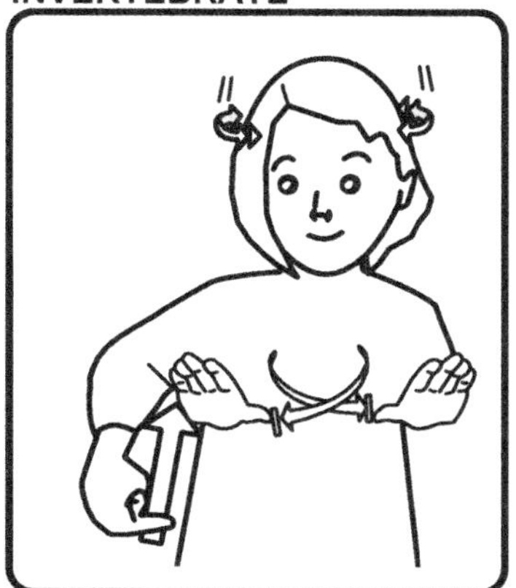

R. index points to backbone then head shakes as crossed flat hands swing apart (**NOT**).

INVESTIGATION

Fingers of palm down 'V' hands flex and make short movements down and apart. Also means **ANALYSE, EXAMINE, EXPLORE.**

IRREVERSIBLE

Palm back 'V' hand in front of body twists over to palm forward with headshake.

ISLAND

Palm left R. 'O' hand moves in horizontal circles or palm down clawed hand makes short movement down. ***Varies.***

JOINT

Fists are held together at the knuckles and may waggle backward and forward against each other. Point to appropriate part of body.

JUICE

Spell 'J' then fingers of palm down hand wiggle as hand moves right (**LIQUID**) near relevant part of body eg. 'gastric' on stomach.

KIDNEYS

Fingerspell 'K' then point to or place clawed hands on appropriate part of body.

KILL, MEAT

Index finger jabs into side of neck. Thumbtip may also be used for **MEAT**. ***Varies.***

LABEL

(Eg. to label a diagram) 'N' hand twists and moves forward from forehead (**NAME**) then 'C' hand moves to the right.

LABEL

(Eg. diagram) Index finger traces line from item to box indicated by index fingers and thumbs in outline shape.

LABORATORY

Fingerspell 'L' 'A' 'B' then index fingers pointing down move in outline shape of room.

LAKE

Tips of 'O' hand brush forward twice on cheek (**WATER**) then R. index pointing down near L. makes large horizontal circle.

LEAF

R. index finger and thumb open and close in outline shape of leaf from tip of L. index finger.

LEATHER

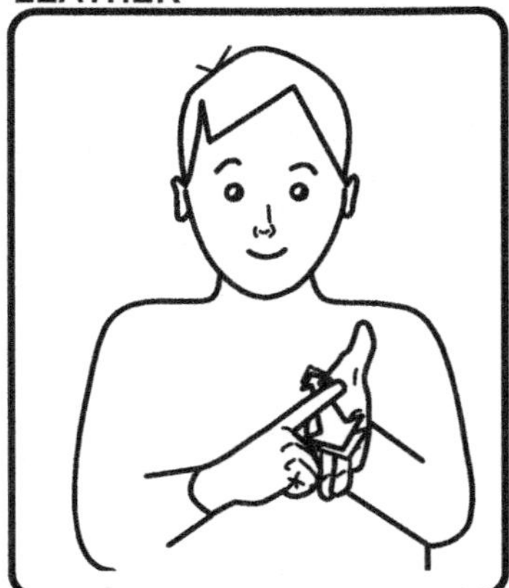

Hands in fingerspelt 'L' formation; R. index finger rubs backwards and forwards on L. palm.

LEG

Index finger points in/down to leg.

LESS, MINIMUM

Palm facing 'N' hand move in/down towards each other. Flat hands may also be used.

LIFE CYCLE

Middle finger tip rubs up and down on side of chest (**LIFE**) then index finger makes large circles in the air (**CYCLE**).

LIGHT (on), PUT LIGHT ON

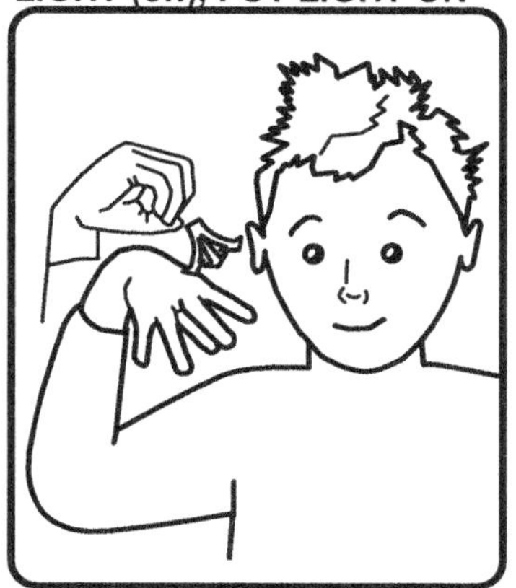

Full 'O' hand (both for plural) springs down/open. Can be ***located*** to suit context. Reverse from open to closed hand for **LIGHT OFF.**

LIGHT (weight)

Palm up open hands make upward wafting movements.

LIGHT BULB

(Eg. in ceiling) Left hand palm down at eye level; R. clawed hand makes action of attaching a light bulb in relevant location.

LIGHTHOUSE

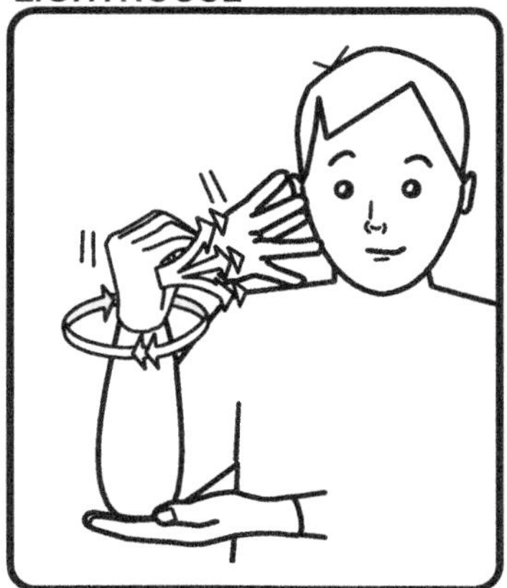

Bunched hand swivels round from the wrist as fingers spring open several times.

LIGHTNING, ELECTRIC/ITY

Palm forward index moves downward sharply in zigzag.

LINE GRAPH

L. 'L' hand held forward; R. index finger traces a line up and down, moving to the right.

LIQUID, FLUID

Palm down hands pointing in move apart with fingers wiggling or full 'C' hand tips over in pouring action.

LIQUID, FLUID

Palm down open hands swish side to side in slight downward arc. Fingers may wiggle slightly.

LISTEN, HEAR

Open hand moves to ear, closing to a bunched hand, or cupped hand held behind ear.

LITMUS PAPER

(Treated test-paper strip turned red by acids, blue by alkalis) R. 'O' hand dips into and out of L. full 'C' hand.

LIVESTOCK

Closed hand with thumb out moves out/down on stomach (**FARM**) then clawed hands move forward alternately (**ANIMAL**).

LIVING ORGANISM

Tip of R. middle finger rubs up/down upper right chest then palm facing hands twist round/down, closing to palm up bunched hands, touching.

LOAD, HEAVY

Palm up hands move simultaneously down with stress to indicate a heavy load.

LOAD, MASS

Palm up hands, one on top of the other, move up and down to indicate a weight or make single firm movement down.

LONG TIME AGO, HISTORY

Bent hands move and circle backwards round each other over the right shoulder.

LOOK, LOOK AT, WATCH

'V' hand (representing eye gaze) moves forward from near eye, or in ***direction*** to suit context. Also means **OBSERVE.**

MAGNET (bar)

Index fingers (or 'N' hands) touch, cheeks sucked in, may then pull apart. Indicates **MAGNETIC ATTRACTION.** ***Varies***

MAGNETIC ATTRACTION

Palm facing 'N' hands flip sharply in/down to touch at tips, cheeks sucked in. ***Varies***

MAGNETISM

(General sign) Fingerspell 'M' with emphasis then pull away, cheeks sucked in. ***Varies***

MAGNETISM (horseshoe)

Press R. 'C' hand on palm of left hand and bounce off with emphasis, cheeks sucked in.

MAINS, PLUG

Bent thumb and fingers of 'V' hand make short firm movement forward or in direction appropriate to context.

MALE, MAN

Fingers and thumb stroke down chin as thumb closes onto fingers. May repeat.

MAN MADE, SYNTHETIC

Fingers and thumb brush down chin, closing (**MAN**) then bunched hands twist against each other (**MAKE**). Also means **ARTIFICIAL.**

MAP

Index fingers move in outline shape of a map or fingerspell 'M' 'A' 'P'.

MASS

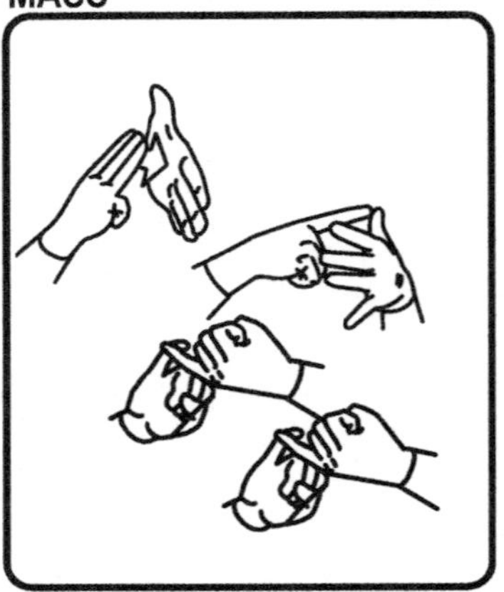

(The amount of solid, liquid or gas in kilograms) Fingerspell 'M' 'A' 'S' 'S' or 'K' 'G'.

MASS

Palm facing clawed hands make a short firm movement down.

MATERIAL/S, FABRIC

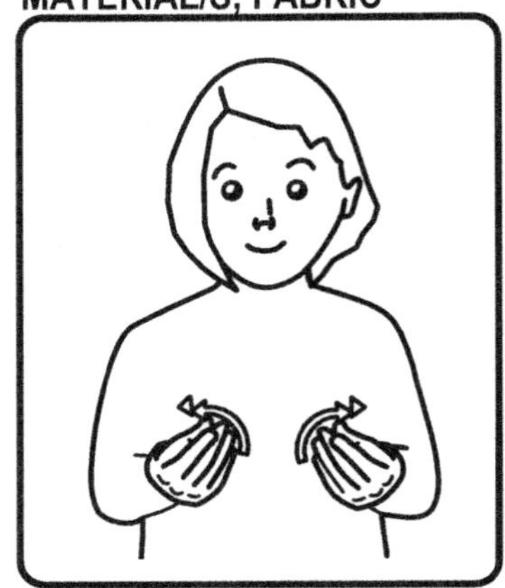

Thumbs rub twice across finger tips of palm up bunched hands.

MATTER

Palm up clawed hands make repeated short downward movements with emphasis.

MEASURE

'O' hands move apart in direction to suit context.

MEASURING CYLINDER

Palm forward extended thumbs; R. moves up, L. down then full 'C' hands one above the other move apart.

MEDIUM, MIDDLE

Blade of R. flat hand taps top of L. middle finger twice.

MEIOSIS

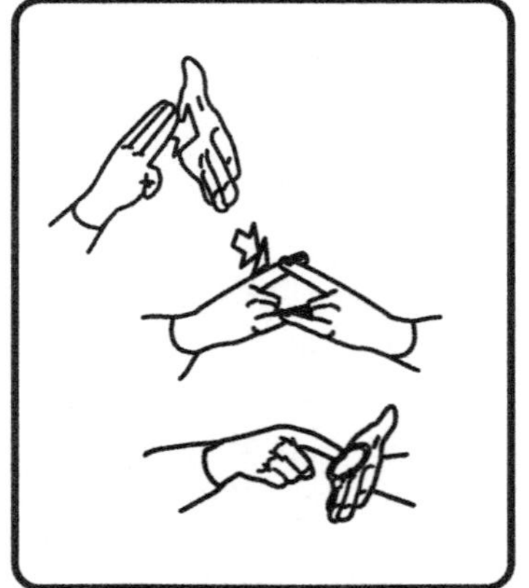

(Division of nucleus when cell divides to form sex cells) Spell 'M' then sign **SEX** and draw small circle on L. palm with R. index (**CELL**).

MELT

Palm facing hands; thumbs rub across fingertips as hands move apart and twist at wrists to finish palm up.

MELTING POINT

R. index moves up behind L. at right angle (**TEMPERATURE**) then thumbs rub across fingertips as hands pull apart (**MELT**).

MENSTRUAL CYCLE

Sign **MENSTRUATION** followed by index finger making circular movements (**CYCLE**) near lower abdomen.

MENSTRUATION

Index finger brushes down off bottom lip then R. open hand brushes down back of L. open hand, located on lower abdomen. ***Varies.***

METAL, STEEL, TIN

Tip of bent index finger taps front of chin twice, lips stretched. Also ***regional*** **GLASS, STONE.**

METAMORPHOSIS

(Transformation from young to adult form) Irish 'T' hands held apart make large slow movement to finish crossed, cheeks puffed.

METHOD, STYLE, SYSTEM

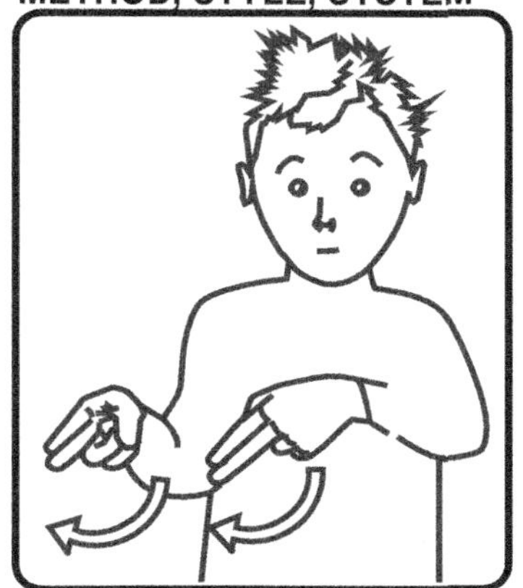

'N' hands (or flat hands) held apart and pointing down twist from the wrists to point and move forward.

MICROSCOPE

R. full 'C' hand behind L. held near eye; hands make inward twisting movements from the wrists.

MILK

Hands move up and down alternately with squeezing actions ('Y' hands can be used) or closed hands rub against each other. ***Varies***.

MITOSIS

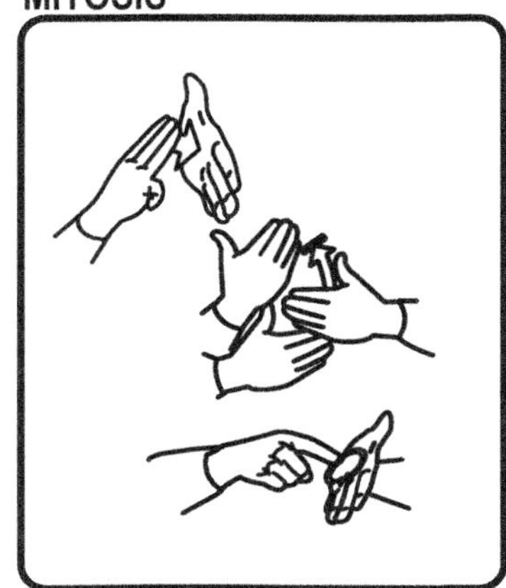

(Division of nucleus when cell divides to make new cells) Spell 'M' then R. flat hand brushes up behind L (**NEW**) then **CELL**.

MIX-UP, CONFUSE

Clawed hands circle round each other, tongue tip between teeth. Also means **COMPLEX, COMPLICATED.**

MIX, MIXTURE

R. open hand palm down above palm up L. hand; hands make alternate circular movements.

MOLECULE

Fingerspell 'M' then index finger and thumb form 'O' hand.

MOMENTUM

(Continuous movement of an object) Palm down closed hands with thumbs extended roll forward round each other. Also means **PROCESS.**

MOMENTUM

(Continuous movement of an object) Spell 'M' then palm down 'C' hands move sideways (**CONTINUE**).

MOON

The index finger and thumb open and close as the hand moves down and round in shape of crescent moon. Also means **LUNAR.**

MORE

R. hand taps twice against knuckles of L. fist. One of several ***variations.***

MOST, MAJORITY

R. index finger brushes forward against side of L. index finger.

MOTION

(Movement of an object) Flat hands move forward circling round each other.

MOUNTAIN

Palm facing flat hands move up and towards each other as they make small repeated twisting movements from the wrists.

MOUSE, MICE

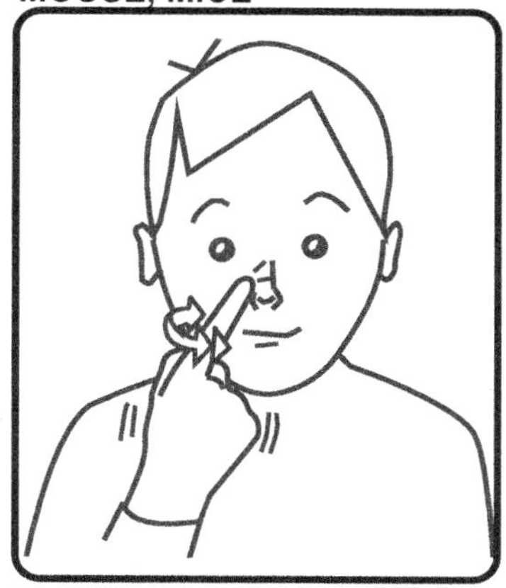

Tip of index finger on side of nose; hand makes quick twisting movements from wrist. A single twist is ***regional*** sign for **PIG**.

MOUTH

Index finger points to mouth.

MOVEMENT

Palm facing hands sweep smoothly sideways.

MUSCLE

Index finger indicates muscle outline on upper arm or appropriate part of body.

MUSCLE

Clawed hand makes squeezing action on upper arm or appropriate part of the body.

NATURAL, NATURE

Repeated fingerspelt initial 'NN'.

NATURE RESERVE

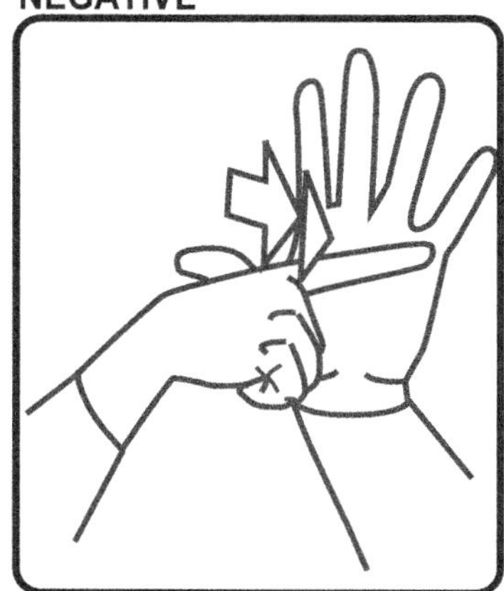

Open hand moves round in horizontal circle (**LAND**), then R. bent hand on L. palm; hands move back to body (**PROTECT**).

NEGATIVE

Edge of R. index finger bangs twice against palm forward L. hand.

NERVE

Index finger pointing back runs up arm towards the brain.

NERVE FIBRE

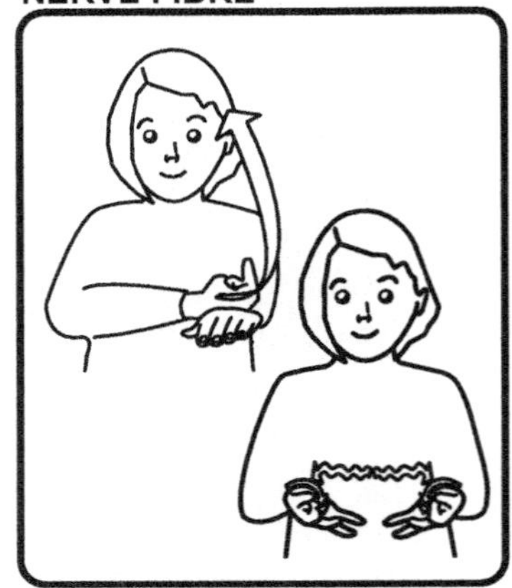

Index finger pointing back runs up arm towards the brain (**NERVE**) then 'O' hands move apart rubbing index and thumb tips (**FIBRE**).

NEUTRALISE

R. flat hand waggles side to side between middle and ring fingers of L. hand. May ***vary.*** Also means **BETWEEN.**

NEUTRON

Fingerspell 'N' then R. full 'O' hand makes short abrupt movement forward (**NOTHING**) to indicate no charge.

NOISE, NOISY, SOUND

Index finger pointing to ear moves in forward circles.

NON-METAL

Tip of bent index finger taps front of chin twice, the lips are stretched and the head shakes.

NORMAL

R. hand of fingerspelt 'N' formation brushes forwards off L. palm twice.

NORTH

Bent hand moves upwards at head height.

NOSE

Index finger contacts nose.

NUCLEUS

(Of a cell) R. index makes circling movement on L. palm (**CELL**) then points to centre of L. palm.

NUCLEUS, NUCLEAR

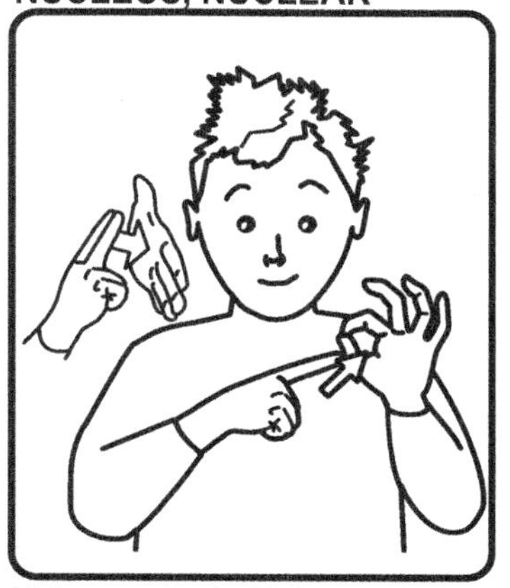

(Of an atom) R. index finger points to centre of L. 'O' hand (**ATOM**).

OCEAN

Palm down open hands move apart in large wavy movements.

OLD, AGED, ELDERLY

Palm back 'V' hand moves down in front of nose. Also ***regional*** **DARK, NIGHT.**

OMNIVORE

(Plant and animal eating) Bunched hand moves to mouth (**EAT**) then opens up behind L. (**PLANT**) and index prods neck (**MEAT**).

ONWARD, ONGOING

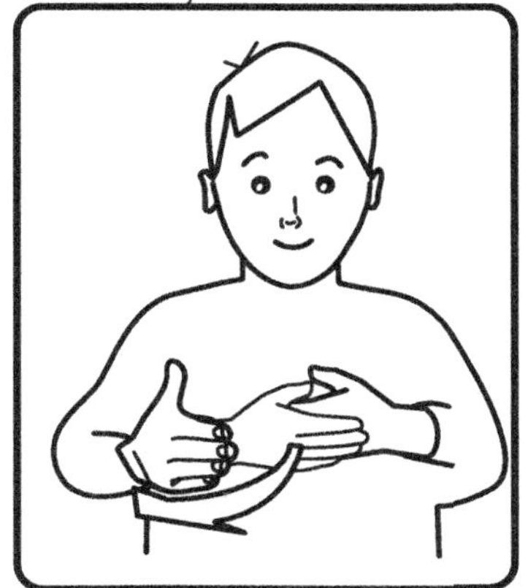

Palm back R. flat hand moves in forward sweep from back of L. flat hand.

ORBIT

(Eg. Earth orbiting Sun) R. index finger circles at an angle round L. full 'O' hand.

ORGAN

(Eg. liver) Place clawed hand on appropriate part of body for organ referred to.

ORGANS

(Eg. liver, heart, kidneys) Place clawed hands on appropriate parts of the body for organs referred to.

OURSELVES

Palm back closed hands with index fingers extended circle alternately backwards to brush down body several times.

OUTPUT

Place R. bunched hand into L. full 'C' hand then out the other side changing to index finger moving out and away.

OVARIES

Palm forward index finger brushes forward on cheek (**WOMAN**) then palm back 'O' hands contact appropriate part of body.

OVUM, EGG CELL

(Unfertilised female reproductive cell produced by the ovary) Full 'O' hand makes short movement forward.

OWL

Hands with bent index, middle finger and thumb (representing eyeballs) twist towards each other.

OXYGEN

Fingerspell 'O' 'X'.

OXYGEN

(The formula of oxygen is O_2) Fingerspell 'O' followed by **2** slightly lower to represent the symbol.

PAPER

Knuckles of closed hands tap together twice. May ***vary.***

PARACHUTE

Palm down R. clawed hand held above L. index finger as formation moves diagonally down.

PARENT/S, PARENTAL

Hands form fingerspelt 'M', then fingerspelt 'F'. Also means **MOTHER, FATHER.**

PARK, SWINGS

Closed hands swing backwards and forwards several times.

PEACOCK

Palm forward full 'O' hands move up/apart as fingers spread open. ***Varies.***

PENGUIN

Palm down flat hands and shoulders make alternate short movements forward/down.

PERIODIC TABLE

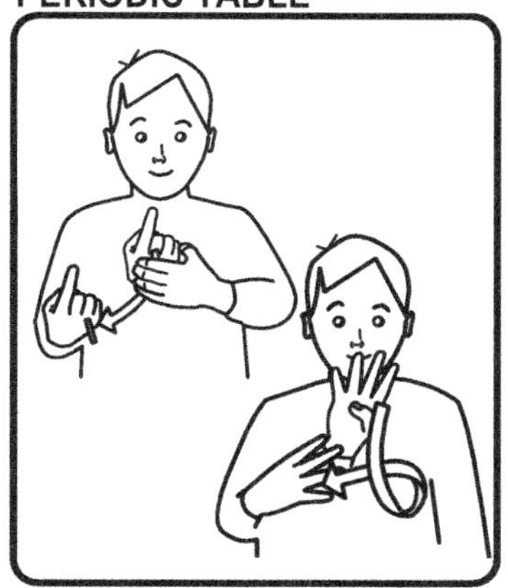

R. index moves down/right behind L. full 'C' (**ELEMENT**) and palm forward open hand, thumb in, moves down and twists over to the right.

PETAL

Tip of R. index finger and thumb on extended L. index finger, make small movement to the right closing to an 'O' hand.

PETROL, GARAGE

'L' hand moves down twisting downwards from the wrist.

PHENOTYPE

Fingerspell 'P' then index (or 'V' hand) moves forward from the eye (**LOOK**) and palm down extended index fingers held together (**LIKE**).

PHOTOSYNTHESIS

(Plant process making food from sunlight) Hand springs open near head (**LIGHT**) then bunched hands twist against each other (**MAKE**).

PHYSICS

Fingerspell 'P' then tap knuckles of palm back bent 'V' hands together twice.

PICK UP, CATCH

Palm forward hands move back to body as fingers close onto thumbs (eg. *catch flu*), or to the head (eg. *pick up facts*).

PITCH

Index finger pointing to ear moves jerkily up and down as it moves to the right.

PIVOT

R. flat hand balances on tips of upright L. flat hand as elbow pivots up and down.

PLANT

R. full 'O' hand moves up as fingers spread open behind L. full 'C' hand. Repeat several times to the right for **PLANTS, VEGETATION.**

PLASTIC

Hands in fingerspelt 'P' formation; R. 'O' hand brushes forward twice off tip of L. index finger. Also one version of **PAPER.**

PLASTIC

R. index finger and thumb grasp top of extended L. index finger and waggle it back and forth.

PLOT (on a graph)

L. 'L' hand held forward as R. bent 'V'; hand makes short forward movements moving to the right.

POINT

Hands in fingerspelt 'P' formation; R. 'O' hand twists forwards on L. extended index finger.

POLLEN

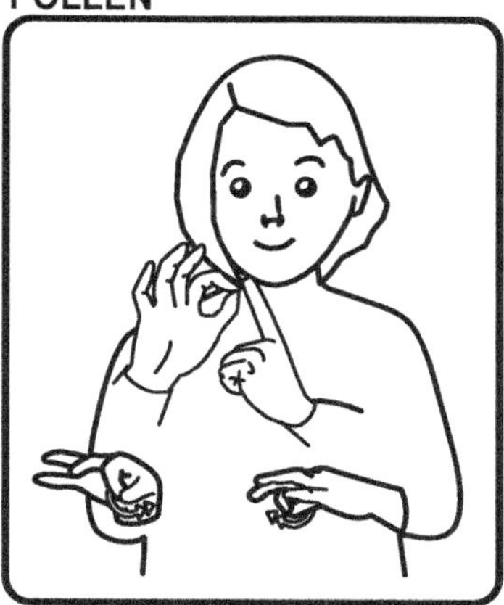

Fingerspell 'P' then palm down 'O' hands rub index and thumb tips together several times (**POWDER**).

POLLINATION

Fingerspell 'P' then palm down 'O' hands rub index and thumb tips together several times (**POWDER**) as they cross over each other.

POLLUTION

Wrists of closed hands rub in circles against each other (**DIRTY**) then palm down open hands move forward/apart (**SPREAD**).

POLLUTION

Open hands rub in circles against each other (**DIRTY**) then palm down open hands move forward/apart (**SPREAD**).

POND

Tips of R. 'O' hand brush forward twice on cheek (**WATER**) then R. index contacts L. and moves round in horizontal circle.

POSITIVE, PLUS

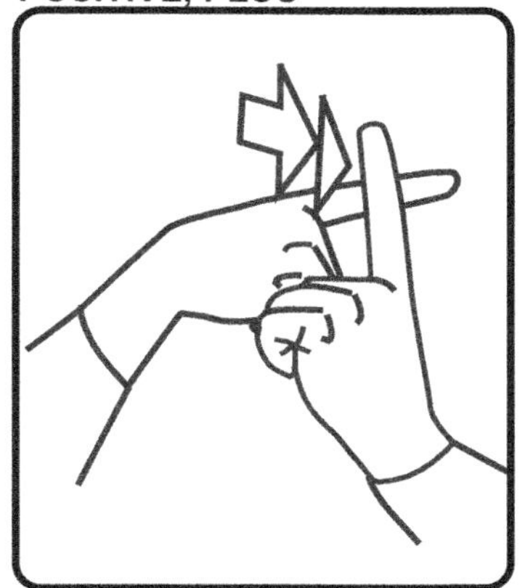

R. index taps twice against L. at right angles.

POWDER

Palm down 'O' hands rub index and thumb tips together several times. With one hand also a version of **SALT**.

POWER

Hands in fists move up/back with emphasis.

PRACTICE, PRACTICAL

Edge of R. flat hand makes short forward chopping movements on L. at right angles.

PRECISE

Tips of R. 'O' hand brush sharply forward against tip of upright L. index finger. One of several ***variations.***

PREDATOR

R. clawed hand moves forward and closes (**BITE**) against L. hand with fierce facial expression.

PREDICT, PREDICTION

Index finger touches side of head (**THINK**) then changes to palm down flat hand moving forward in an arc (**FUTURE**).

PRESSURE

Fists held apart move in towards each other with emphasis, cheeks puffed. Will ***vary*** in context. Also means **COMPRESSION.**

PRESSURE

R. flat hand pushes forward twice against L. hand (or index finger) with emphasis, cheeks puffed. Will ***vary*** in context.

PREVENT, PREVENTION

Heel of R. closed hand pushes firmly against horizontal L. index finger. Also means **PROTECT, RESIST.**

PREY

R. clawed hand grasps L. hand with fierce facial expression (**PREDATOR**) then R. index points to L. hand - or fingerspell in full.

PRIMARY CONSUMER

R. flat hand moves left to bang against L. thumb (**FIRST**) or see also **PRIMARY**. Then bunched hand moves to mouth twice (**EATER).**

PRIMARY, FIRST, INITIAL

Palm forward extended index finger twists to palm back in firm upward movement. Also means **PRIORITY.**

PROFESSIONAL

Tip of R. middle finger contacts back of L. hand near wrist then bounces off again.

PROPERTY

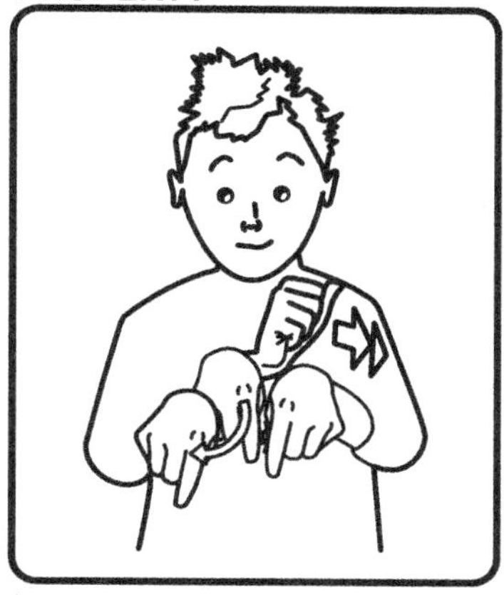

(A special quality) R. index finger brushes forward sharply against L. (**SPECIAL**) then closed hand faces and moves to referent (**OWN**).

PROTECT, RESCUE, SAVE

R. bent hand on L. palm as hands move back to body. Also means **SAFE, SAFETY.**

PROTON

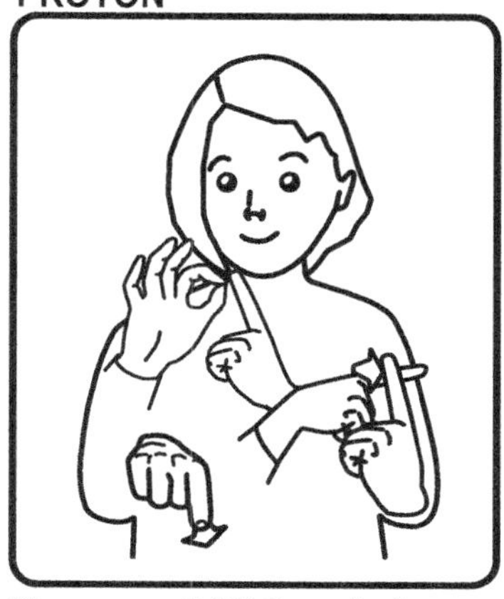

Fingerspell 'P' then index fingers held crossed (**POSITIVE** charge) and R. index jabs forward (proton in middle of atom).

PUBERTY

Open hands pat down body several times (**BODY**) then Irish 'T' hands move upwards and cross over each other (**CHANGE**).

PULL, DRAG, FORCE

Irish 'T' hands move back/right in pulling action. ***Varies*** in context.

PURE

Palm forward 'O hands make short firm movement forward.

RABBIT

Palm forward 'N' hands held at sides of head twitch forwards several times. Also one version of **HARE.**

RADIATION

(Eg. grill) Full 'O' hands open and move down or forward in direction to suit context.

RADIATION

(Eg. radiation from the sun) R. full 'O' hand springs open as it moves in/down from head height and continues to move down.

RADIOACTIVE/ITY

Fingerspell 'R' then fists held together twist in snapping movement (**BREAK**) and palm down open hands move forward/apart (**SPREAD**).

RAIN, DRIZZLE

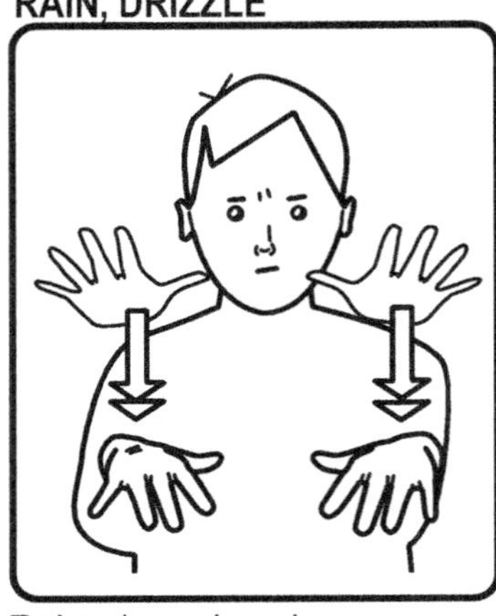

Palm down hands move down twice, fingers may wiggle (**DRIZZLE**) or hands move sideways with force, cheeks puffed (**HEAVY RAIN**).

RAINBOW

Palm forward full 'C' hand moves over in large arc. Also means **ARCH, BRIDGE.**

RAINCOAT

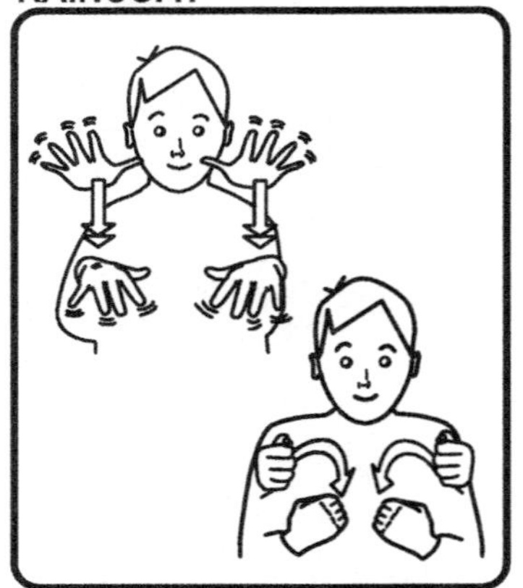

(Waterproof) Open hands make two movements down (**RAIN**) then closed hands move down from shoulders in front of body (**COAT**).

RATE OF REACTION

Clawed hands circle alternately or R. index moves sharply up (**REACTION**) and R. index finger taps up and down on top of L. (**SPEED**).

REACT, REACTION

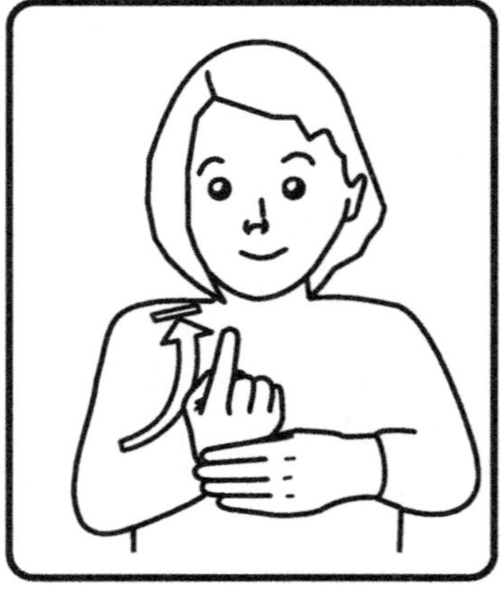

R. index finger moves sharply up behind palm back L. flat hand.

REACT, REACTION

Palm facing clawed hands make alternate forward circling movements.

REACTIVITY

(Readiness to react) Index fingertip taps cheek twice (**EASY**) then R. index finger moves sharply up behind L. flat hand (**REACT**).

RECESSIVE

(Opposite of dominant) Edge of extended R. little finger brushes down left upper arm. Also means **WEAK.**

RECOGNISE, IDENTIFY

R. flat hand moves forward to contact L. index finger, and bounces back again. ***Directional.***

RECORD

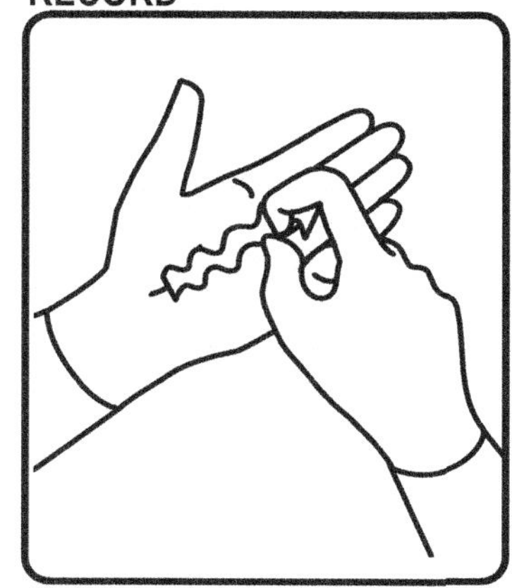

R. hand moves along L. palm with squiggling movements. Also means **TAKE NOTES.**

RECORD, MAKE NOTES

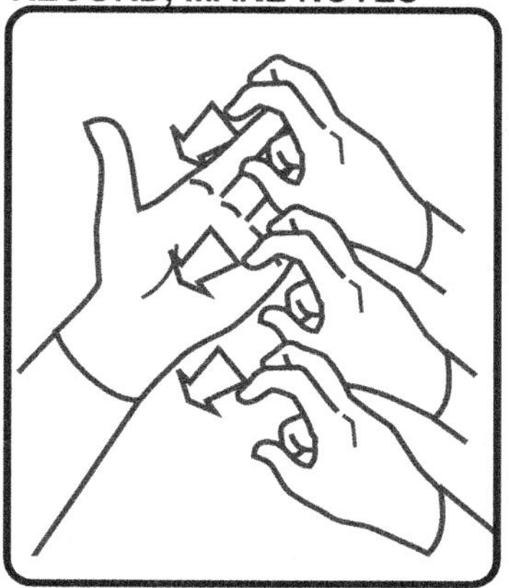

Tips of bent 'V' hand (or 'N' hand) make short movements towards L. palm several times, moving down.

RECYCLE

Palm left R. 'V' hand makes two clockwise circular movements.

REDUCE, REDUCTION

Palm facing flat hands move down/in towards each other.

REFLECT, REFLECTION

(Eg. light bouncing off a surface) R. index finger moves from near eye to L. palm and bounces back again. Will ***vary*** in context.

REFRACTION

(Light 'bends' through glass or water) R. index finger moves between L. hand middle and ring fingers and then bends on exit.

RELEASE, FREE

Closed hands held together crossed at wrists spring open and apart.

REPEL

(Eg. in magnetism, opposite of attract) Fingers move towards each other and bounce apart. Handshape ***varies*** for type of magnet.

REPLY, RESPOND, ANSWER

R. index near mouth flicks forward, as L. index held forward flicks back. ***Directional***.

REPRODUCTION

(General term) Tips of fingers of bunched hands twist against each other as hands move upwards. Also means **CONSTRUCT, CREATE**.

REPRODUCTION

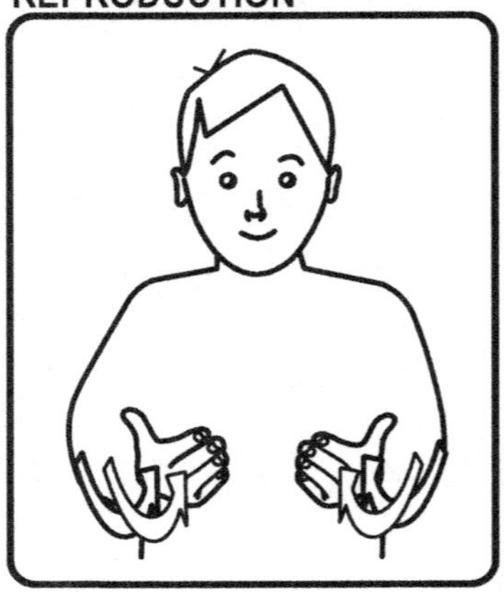

(Eg. human) Palm up flat hands move forward from sides of body (**BIRTH**) and repeats.

REPRODUCTION

(Eg. plant) R. full 'O' hand moves up as fingers spread open behind L. full 'C' hand (**PLANT**) and repeats.

RESEARCH

Palm down bent 'V' hands make two short movements down and apart as fingers flex.

RESISTANCE

(To slow down the flow of electricity) Palm forward fists crossed at the wrists make firm movement forward. ***Varies.*** Also means **PROOF.**

RESPIRATION

(How living things obtain energy from food and oxygen) Fingerspell 'R' then fists move up/back to chest twice (**ENERGY**).

REST, COMFORTABLE

Hands (or one hand) move back, thumbs onto chest, head tilted, lips pushed forward. Also means **BREAK, AT EASE, HOLIDAY.**

RESULT

Fingers of palm back open hands wiggle as hands move downwards. ***Varies.***

REVERSIBLE

Palm back 'V' hand twists to palm forward with headnod.

RIBS

Tips of clawed hands pull apart on front of chest to indicate the ribcage. Also one version of **SKELETON.**

RIGHT, CORRECT

R. closed hand with thumb out moves down to contact L. palm.

RISK/Y, APPREHENSIVE

Tips of 'O hand tap into neck twice, lips stretched with teeth clenched.

RIVER, STREAM

'N' hands held apart move forwards with simultaneous side to side wavy movements.

ROCK

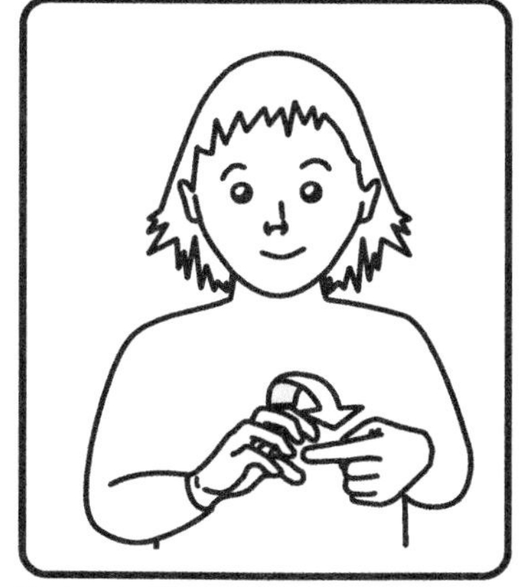

Clawed hands held facing; R. hand twists forwards. May ***vary*** in context.

ROCK, STONE, COAL

Palm left R. clawed hand twists forward over tip of L. index finger held pointing to the right.

ROOT

R. full 'O' hand held under L. palm down hand; R. hand fingers spring open.

ROOTS

Palm down fists spring open downwards and outwards.

ROPE

Fists held together twist alternately from wrists as they move apart.

ROTATE

Flat hands rotate round each other. Will ***vary*** in context. Index fingers may also be used.

ROTTEN, POLLUTED

Edge of R. extended little finger rubs in circles on L. palm with negative expression. Also means **CORRUPTED.**

ROUGH

Edge of R. bent index finger brushes sharply to the right across the chin or tips of clawed hand rub arm. May ***vary*** in context.

ROUNDABOUT

R. index points down and L. index points up as they circle round each other.

RUN, RUNNER, JOG/GER

Closed hands make alternate forward/up and down/back movements at sides of body.

SALT

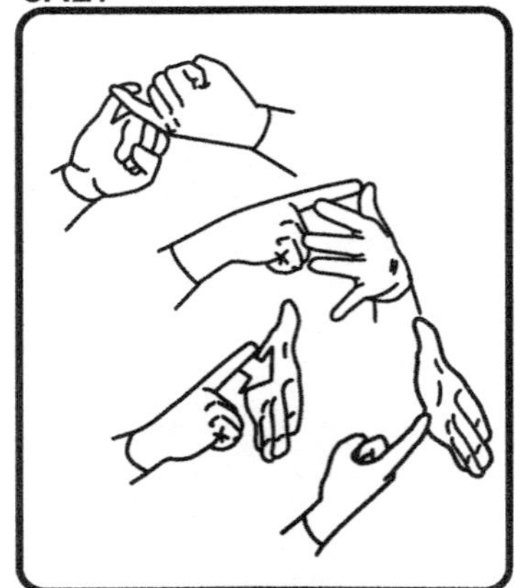

Fingerspell 'S' 'A' 'L' 'T'.

SAME, SIMILAR, LIKE

Index fingers pointing forward are held together with single contact or may tap twice. Also means **ALSO, TOO.**

SAMPLE

Thumb and fingertips of R. bent hand touch L. palm then move to the right as fingers close onto thumb.

SAND, SOIL

Thumbs rub across pads of fingers in crumbling action as hands move upwards.

SATELLITE

R. extended index finger bounces down and off L. palm. Also one version of **REFLECTING**.

SATURATED

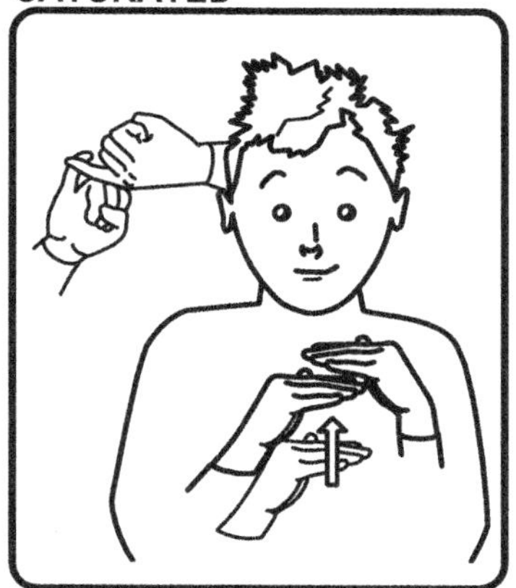

Fingerspell 'S' then R. bent hand moves up to contact the underside of L. bent hand (**FULL**).

SAVE, SAVE UP, COLLECT

R. bent hand brushes back to body twice across L. palm. Single movement for **SAFE, SAFETY.**

SCALES, BALANCE

Palm up flat hands move alternately up and down. Also one version of **RATIO.**

SCIENCE, EXPERIMENT

Full 'C' hands make alternate tipping movements in front of the body. Handshapes may ***vary*** eg. 'O' hands or bent 'V' hands may also be used.

SCREENING

R. hand with index, little finger and thumb extended moves down from eye, then 'Y' hands twist alternately from wrists moving left.

SEA, WATER

Palm down open hand moves sideways in wavy up and down motion. Can be both hands. Also one version of **FLOAT.**

SEAL

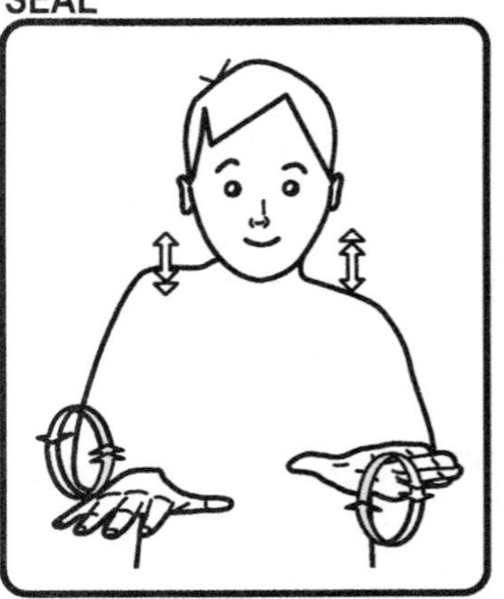

Palm down hands turned out make alternate forward circling movements as shoulders move up and down alternately.

SEASONS

Palm facing flat hands move simultaneously down, then repeat three times, moving to the right.

SEED

Palm down 'O' hand rubs index and thumb tips together. Also one version of **SALT**, and with short movement down, to **PLANT.**

SEEDS

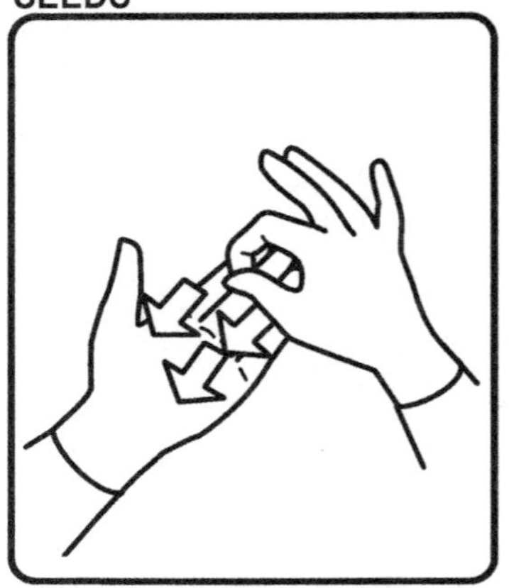

Tips of R. 'O' hand tap down across L. palm. R. hand moves forward/down from L. palm for **PLANT.**

SENSE, THE SENSES

Fingers of palm down open hands wiggle as hands move alternately backwards and forwards to the face.

SEPARATE, PART

Finger of bent hands start back to back, then move apart.

SEX

Hands closed, index and little fingers extended and in contact, tap together twice (based on fingerspelt formation **SX**).

SEX

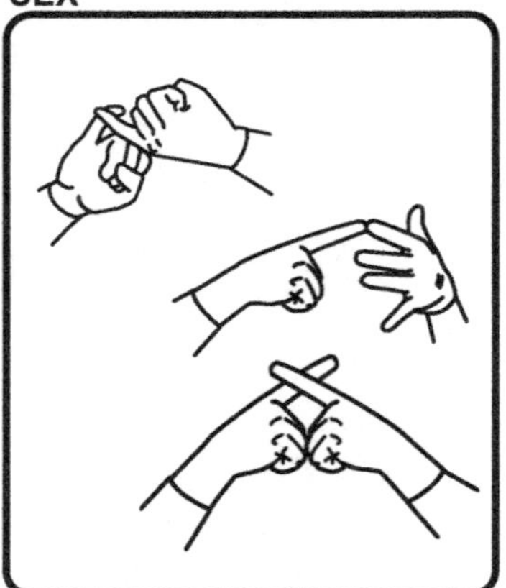

Fingerspell 'S' 'E' 'X'.

SEX

Bent hands with thumbs extended bang together with thumbs interlocking. One of several ***variations.***

SHADOW

Palm forward open hands make inward circular movements, one if front of the other, in front of the face. ***Directional.***

SHAPE

Palm facing open hands held apart move in and out to indicate a shape. Can also be signed with index fingers and ***varies*** in context.

SHEEP

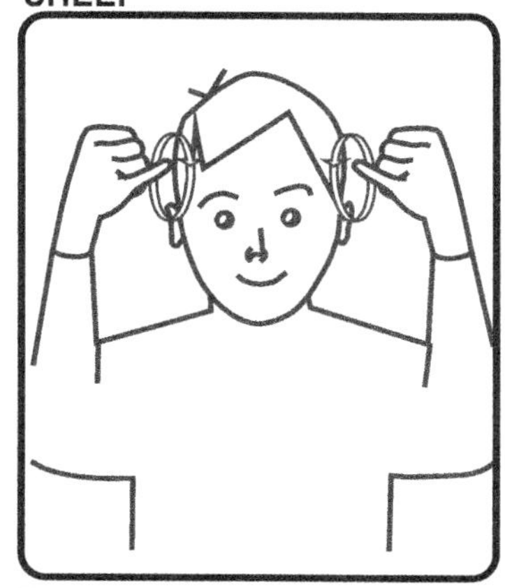

Extended little fingers make forward circles from sides of head. Can be one hand or two.

SHINY

Palm facing open hands move upwards twisting quickly from the wrists.

SHIP

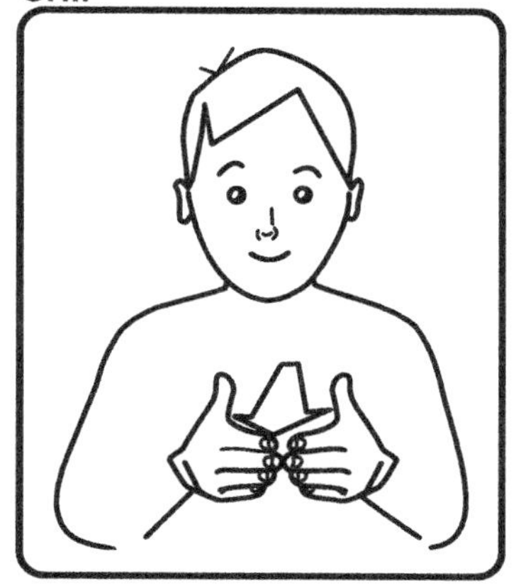

Flat hands held at an angle and touching at the tips, move forward. With bobbing up and down movements means **BOAT.**

SIGHT, SEE

(The sense of sight) Index finger moves forward from eye. Can also be signed with 'V' hand (eye-gaze classifier).

SILVER

Hands form fingerspelt 'S', then hands spring open and apart.

SINCE, FROM THEN ON

Palm back R. bent hand moves forward/down from right shoulder to contact palm of palm back L. hand held forward.

SINK, DROWN

R. hand with fingers spread closes sharply to a bunched hand as it moves down between thumb and fingers of L. full 'C' hand.

SKELETON

Tips of narrow 'C' hands move apart across chest, move down, and repeat. Also means **BONES.**

SKIP, SKIPPING

Palm up Irish 'T' hands make simultaneous forward circular movements at sides of body.

SLIDE, CHUTE

Palm down flat hand sweeps down/left. A straight downward sloping movement for **SLOPE.**

SLOW, SLOWLY, AGES

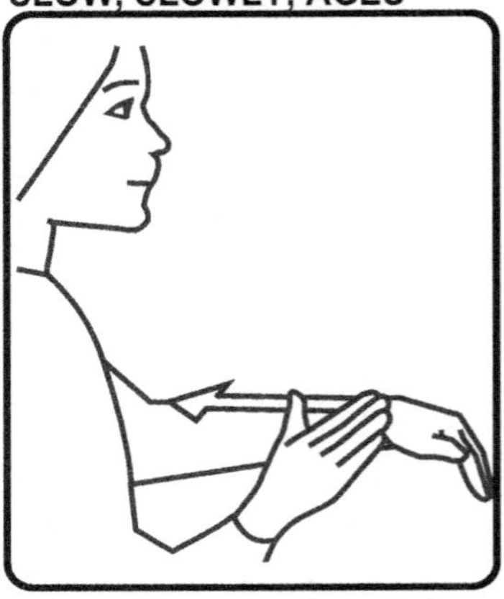

R. hand brushes from left wrist up the forearm. Also means **LONG TIME.**

SMELL

(The sense of smell) Fingers of palm down open hand wiggle as hand moves backwards to the nose.

SMOOTH

Palm down R. flat hand brushes smoothly along back of palm down L. hand.

SNAIL

R. 'V' hand pushes forward/up from under L. bent hand or index fingers held on sides of forehead flex forward/up. ***Varies.***

SNOW, SNOWING

Fingers wiggle as hands move down in small wavy movements. Cheeks puffed for **HEAVY SNOW.**

SOFT

Index finger prods gently into the cheek twice.

SOFT, SPONGY, SPRINGY

Thumb opens and closes onto fingers several times. Both hands may be used.

SOIL, EARTH

Palm down bunched hands rub thumbs across fingertips twice. Also means **FLOUR, POWDER.** With one hand also one version of **SALT.**

SOLID

Palm facing clawed hands held slightly apart make short firm movement down.

SOLUBLE

'C' hand moves forward closing from nose as head nods (**CAN**) then thumbs rub across fingertips as hands move apart (**DISSOLVE**).

SOLUTION

'O' hand (or flat hand) moves in action of stirring (**STIR**) then thumbs rub across fingertips as hands move apart (**DISSOLVE**).

SOME, FEW, SEVERAL

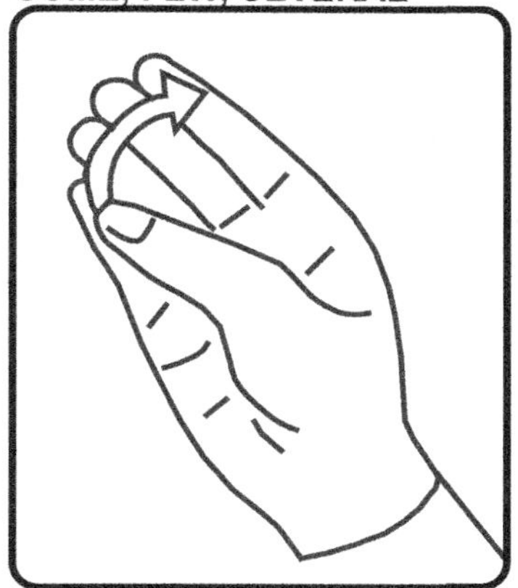

Thumb rubs across pads of fingers.

SOMETIMES, IRREGULAR

'Y' hands twist alternately from the wrists as the hands move right. Also means **SHIFTS.**

SOUTH

Palm down hand makes downward movement at side of body.

SPACE

Palm forward 'O' hands stretch upwards and open wide.

SPECIES

Palm facing clawed hands held apart move to contact each other. May repeat moving sideways.

SPEED

R. index finger bounces up and down on L. twice. Also means **FAST, QUICK, HURRY.** ***Varies.***

SPEED OF LIGHT

R. full 'O' springs open near head (**LIGHT**) then straight 'C' hand shoots sharply forward, fingers snap shut, cheeks puffed (**SPEED**).

SPEED, SHARP

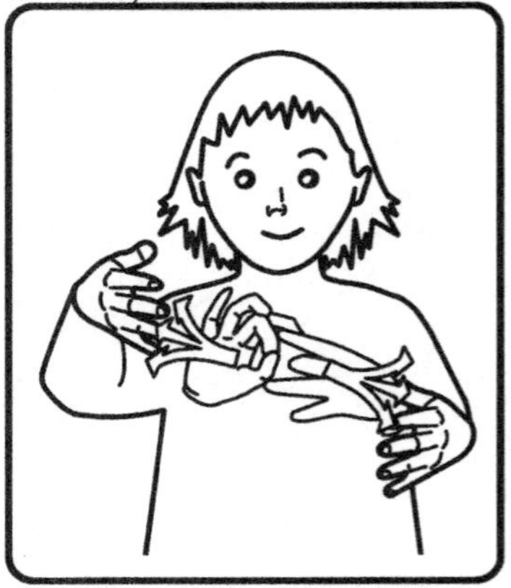

Palm facing hands held near each other with middle fingers flexed on thumbs, pull diagonally apart and open sharply.

SPERM

Fingerspell 'S' then R. index finger wiggles forward or to the side.

SPIDER

Fingers of palm down clawed hand wiggle as the hand moves forward.

SPILL

Full 'O' hands move sharply down/forward and spring open. Also means **LOSE, LOST** and one version of **WASTE, WASTEFUL.**

SPIN, TURN

Index finger makes quick circling movements (in direction to suit context). Slow movement for **TURN.**

SPINE

Index finger points backwards/down over shoulder, then narrow 'C' hands move apart.

SPRING, GROW, DEVELOP

R. open hand swivels from pointing down to being upright behind palm back L. flat hand. ***Varies.***

SQUIRREL

Full 'C' hand moves in upward/outward arc from side of body. Also used for **TAIL.**

STABLE

(To maintain equilibrium) Palm down R. extended bent index hooks down onto palm up L. bent index as formation moves forward/right.

STANDARD PRESSURE

Palm down flat hands move together in wide circle (**STANDARD**) then palm back bent hands at sides of head move down slightly twice.

STERILE

Edge of R. flat hand lands emphatically on L. palm, then brushes forward with emphasis as mouth opens then closes.

STORM, GALE, STORMY

Flat hands at sides of head sway from side to side.

STRONG, ENERGY

Clenched fists move upwards as arms bend at the elbows. Arms may move out sideways. Also means **CONCENTRATED, POWER.**

STRUCTURE, CONSTRUCT

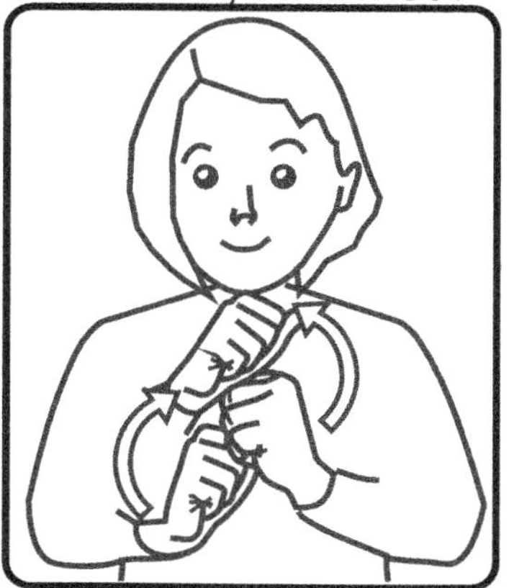

Palm facing closed hands move alternately upwards, one on top of the other.

SUBSTANCE

Fingerspell 'S' then thumb tips rub twice across fingertips (**MATERIAL**).

SUMMER, HOT WEATHER

Flat hand (or index finger) strokes left to right across forehead. ***Regional.***

SUN, SUNNY, SUNSHINE

Full 'O' hand moves down/in as the fingers spring open at head height. Also means **SOLAR.**

SUNRISE

R. full 'O' hand moves in upward arc from behind left arm held across front of body.

SUNSET

R. full 'O' hand held upright above left arm held in front of body, moves right in downward arc.

SURVIVE

Tip of middle finger brushes upwards twice on side of upper chest (**LIVE**) then palm down 'C' hands move to the right or forward (**CONTINUE**).

SUSTAINABLE

Two palm forward/down 'C' hands move simultaneously to the right and repeat several times in circular movements.

SWERVE

Flat hand pointing forwards swings slightly right then left in swerving movement. Can vary in context.

SYMBOL

(Eg. Calcium - Ca) 'N' hand touches forehead and moves/twists forward (**NAME**) then thumbs make short movement in (**SHORT**).

SYNDROME

Palm facing hands with fingers curved in move down twisting round to finish palm up bunched hands in contact.

TABLE, GRAPH

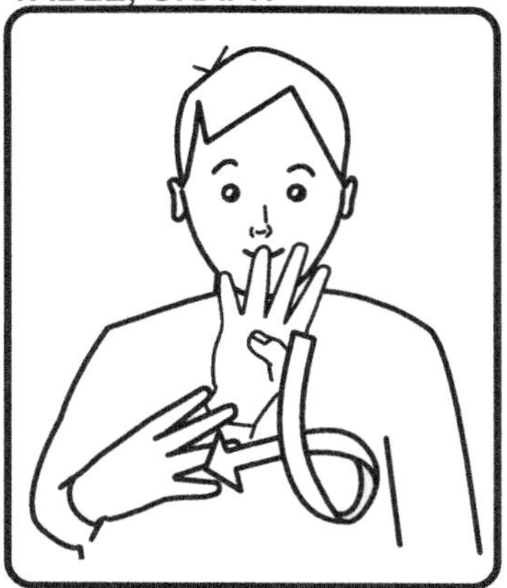

Palm forward open hand with thumb tucked in moves down, twists over to palm back and moves right. Also means **TIMETABLE**.

TASTE

(The sense of taste) Index finger makes two small movements to the mouth, tongue protrudes slightly.

TEETH

Index finger moves across left to right in front of the mouth, teeth exposed.

TELESCOPE

Full 'C' hands R. in front of L. held near eyes; R. hand moves forward/up.

TEMPERATURE

R. index pointing left brushes up and down against upright L. index finger. Also means **THERMOMETER.**

TEND, CARE FOR

Index moves down from near eye then changes to bent hand tapping twice on L. bent hand. Also means **LOOK AFTER.**

TENSION

Clenched fists pull apart twice with stress, lips stretched.

TEST TUBE

Narrow 'C' hands held R. above L. then L. hand moves downwards.

THEORY, THEORETICAL

Fingers of palm down open hand wiggle as hand moves repeatedly backwards and forwards from forehead.

THERMAL INSULATION

(Eg. of a house) R. clawed hand moves across mouth (**HEAT**) then clawed hands move in outline shape of house or other in context.

THERMOMETER

'O' hands (or narrow 'C' hands) held R. above L. then R. hand moves up a short way in outline shape.

THERMOMETER

'O' hand makes a short movement forward from mouth and then makes repeated downward shaking movements.

THICK, DENSE

Palm forward full 'C' hand makes short firm movement forward.

THIN (person)

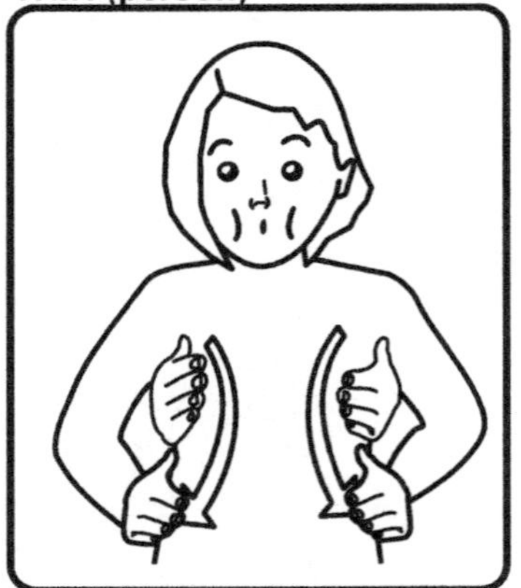

Hands move in and down the sides of the body with cheeks sucked in.

THIN, NARROW

Palm forward narrow 'C' hand moves downwards.

THING, SOMETHING, ITEM

Palm back closed hands with index fingers up bang together twice.

THINK

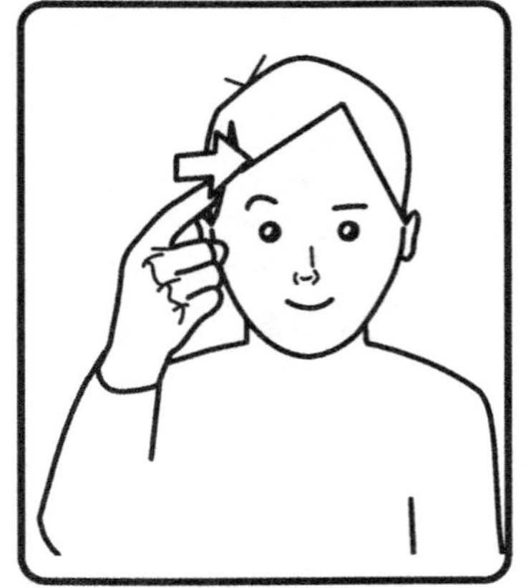

Index finger taps or makes circular movements on side of forehead. May tap twice also meaning **BRAIN, MIND, SENSIBLE.**

THROUGH

Fingers of palm left R. flat hand pass through middle and ring fingers of L. hand.

THRUST, FORCE

R. fist pushes forcefully forward against palm back L. hand, cheeks puffed. **THRUST** can be R. hand part of sign only.

THUNDER, STORM/Y

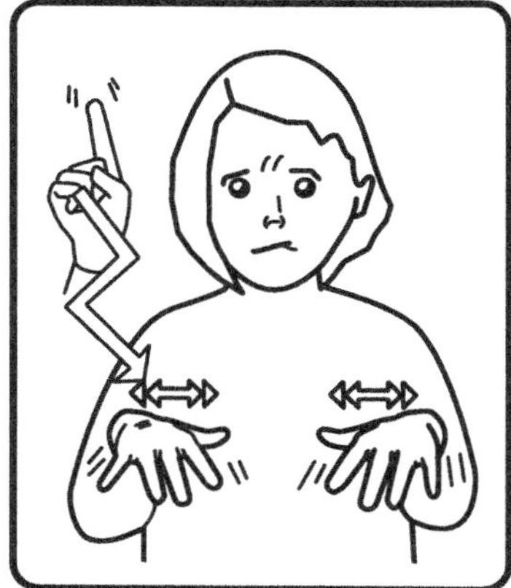

Palm forward index moves down in sharp zigzag then palm down open hands shake from side to side several times.

TOES

Hands held palm down in front of hips with fingers wiggling.

TORCH

Palm up 'C' hand sweeps side to side several times in an arc.

TORTOISE

Bent hands, palms facing outwards, make short alternate movements forward/sideways. ***Varies.***

TOTAL

Clawed hands held palm facing, one above the other, come together and touch as fingers close into bunched hands.

TOUCH

(The sense of touch and feeling) Fingers of R. flat hand make a light touch on back of L. hand. R. brushes along back of L. for **FEEL.**

TRAIN, RAILWAY

Closed hand (or fist) makes firm forward movement from side of body.

TRANSPARENT

Fingers of R. hand pass through fingers of L. hand held forward. May start with index moving forward from eye (***SEE***).

TREE

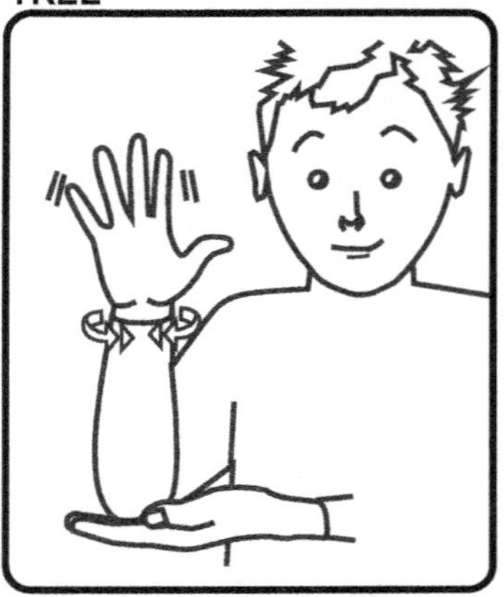

R. open hand upright and resting on L. hand, twists repeatedly from the wrist.

TROPICAL FOREST

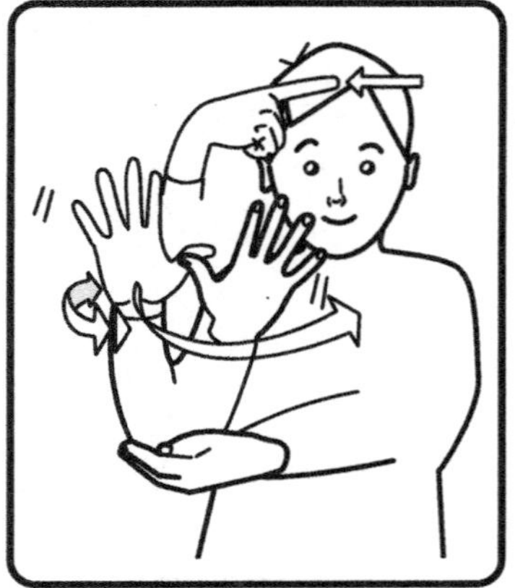

R. index is drawn across forehead (**HOT**) then open hand with elbow on L. palm swings round in arc in front of body (**FOREST**).

TRY, ATTEMPT

R. extended index finger brushes forward twice against L.

TSUNAMI, TIDAL WAVE

Palm left open hands sweep up, over and and to the left.

TURN, TURN ROUND

Palm back R. closed hand (held with elbow on back of L. hand) twists sharply to palm forward. Represents the head turning.

TWIST

Fists held together twist against each other. Will ***vary*** in context.

TWIST, TURN, OPEN

(Eg. open a jar) R. clawed hand held above L. full 'C' hand makes clockwise twisting movement. May ***vary*** in context.

UNDERNEATH, BELOW

Palm down R. flat hand makes circular movements below palm down L. flat hand.

UNHEALTHY

Fingertips touch chest then move forward changing to closed hands, thumbs up, as the head shakes, lips pressed together.

UNNATURAL

Fingerspell 'N' and tap twice on L. palm as the head shakes, lips pressed together.

UNSTABLE

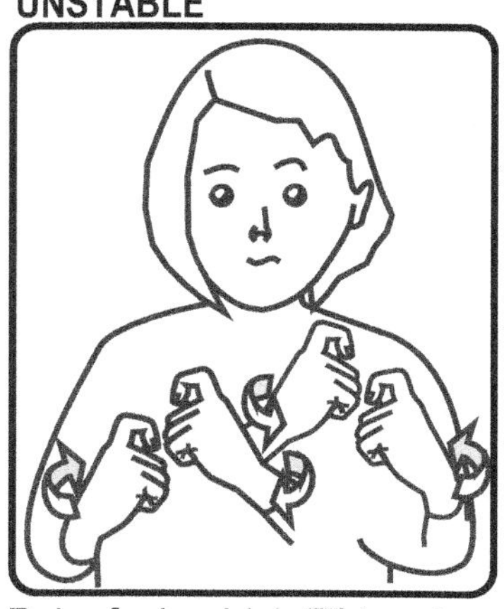

Palm facing Irish 'T' hands twist alternately as they move to the right. The lips are stretched.

UP, UPWARDS, NORTH

Index finger points up and makes small upward movement. Repeated movement for **UPSTAIRS.**

US, WE

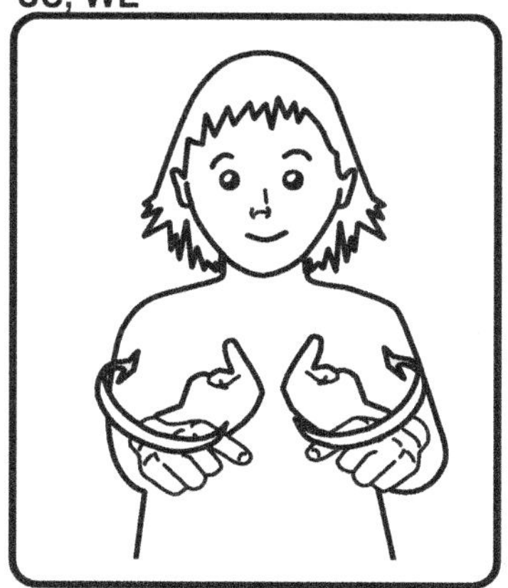

Index fingers pointing forwards twist round, apart and back, to finish in contact with chest. Can be one hand only.

VACUUM

(Said to exist in a region without matter) Hands fan back to face (**AIR**); flat hand brushes sharply past mouth as head shakes (**NOT ANY**).

VACUUM

Palm facing open hands pull apart snapping closed to bunched hands with cheeks sucked in.

VACUUM CLEANER

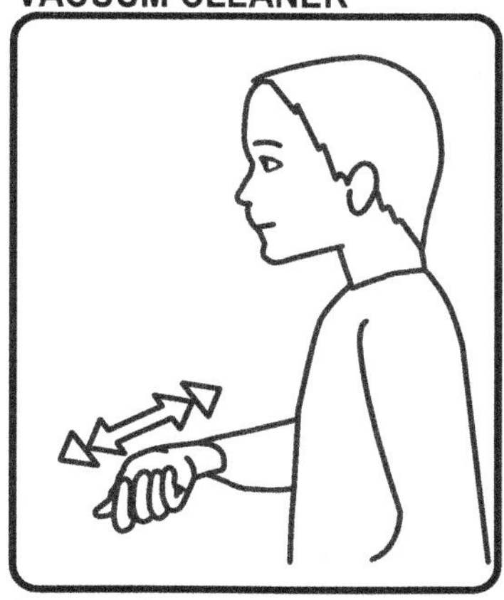

Palm left R. Irish 'T' hand pushes and pulls forward/down and back/up several times.

VALLEY

Palm down flat hands held at shoulder height twist in/down to palms facing out in downward movement towards each other.

VAPOUR

Fingers open and close onto thumbs several times (**WET**) then palm up open hands move up, fingers wiggling, or hands waft upwards.

VARIABLE, VARIATION

Index fingers move alternately up and down as both hands move sideways in front of body. Also means **ASSORTED, DIVERSE.**

VARIOUS, RANGE

R. index finger repeatedly brushes forward against L. as both move to the right in front of body. Also means **ALL KINDS OF, ETC.**

VEGETABLE, VEGETARIAN

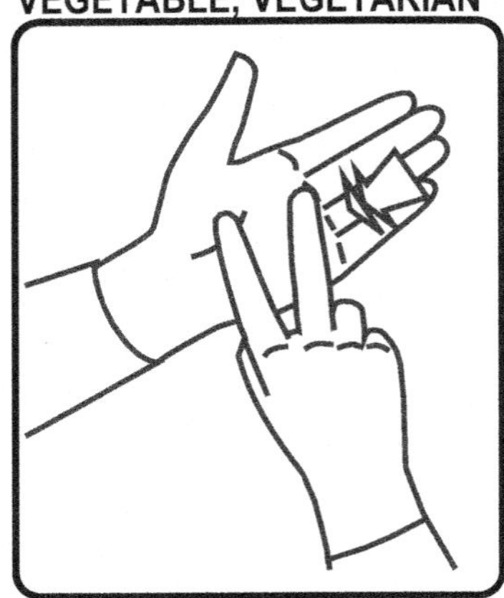

Hands form fingerspelt 'V' and tap twice or fingerspelt abbreviation 'V' 'E' 'G'.

VEIN

Fingerspell 'V' then R. index finger traces wiggly line up left arm from the wrist.

VERTEBRATE

Palm up open hand snaps shut (**HAVE**), R. flat hand moves over shoulder, then narrow 'C' hands pull apart as head nods.

VERTEBRATE

Fingerspell 'V' then R. index pointing back indicates the backbone as the head nods.

VIBRATION

Palm down open hands tremble and twist repeatedly from the wrists.

VIBRATIONS

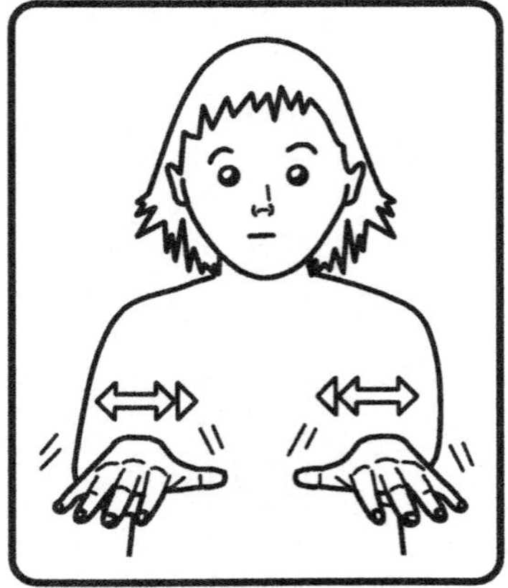

Palm down open hands shake in and out or alternately forward/back several times.

VIRUS

Fingerspell 'V' then palm down open hands wiggle as hands move forward/apart (**SPREAD**).

VIRUS

(Eg. catch a virus) Fingerspell 'V' then palm down open hands move back to contact body closing to bunched hands.

VITAMIN

Fingerspell initial 'V' followed by index finger and thumb flicking open near mouth twice (**TABLET**).

VOICE

Tips of 'N' hand tap twice into throat. Index finger or 'V' hand may alternatively be used.

VOLATILE

Palm up open hands move quickly upwards with fingers wiggling. R. index tapping up and down on L. (**QUICKLY**) can be added.

VOLTMETER

Fingerspell 'V' (also **VOLT, VOLTAGE**) then R. index finger waggles back and forth across L. palm (**METER**).

VOLUME

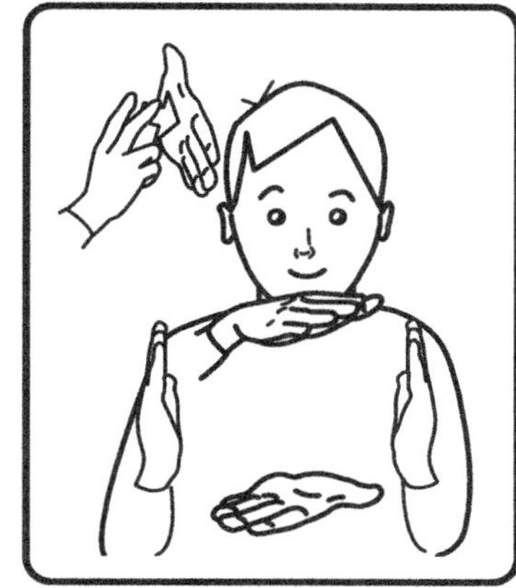

(Space occupied by body or mass of fluid) Fingerspell 'V' then palm facing flat hands indicate shape of cube or other relevant shape.

WALK, ON FOOT

Fingers of 'V' hand (legs classifier) wiggle as hand moves forward or in ***direction*** to suit context. ***Varies.***

WARM

Clawed hand makes small circling movements in front of mouth. Flat hand can also be used. ***Varies.***

WASP

R. 'O' hand moves left with wiggling movements to contact back of L. hand with a sharp jab and bounce off.

WASTE, WASTEFUL

Palm up (or can be palm down) full 'O' hands spring sharply down/ apart as the fingers spring open.

WATER

(The formula for water is H_2O) Fingerspell 'H' then sign **2** slightly lower, followed by an 'O' hand or fingerspelt 'O'.

WATER

Tips of palm forward 'O' hand (or thumb tip of 'Y' hand) brush forward/down twice on side of cheek. ***Varies regionally.***

WATER CYCLE

Tips of R. 'O' hand brush forward/down on cheek (**WATER**) then index finger moves in circular movements (**CYCLE**).

WATER DISPERSAL

'O' hand brushes twice forward/down on cheek (**WATER**) then palm down open hands make wavy movements out/apart.

WATERFALL

Palm down open hands with fingers wiggling move down and right in flowing movement.

WATERPROOF

'O' hand brushes twice forward/down on cheek (**WATER**) then fists crossed at the wrists make short firm movement forward (**RESIST**).

WAVELENGTH

R. index finger moves sideways in wavy movement then two 'L' hands, or palm facing flat hands, pull apart (**LENGTH, LONG**).

WAVES

Palm down open hands move sideways in up and down wavy movements.

WEIGH, WEIGHT

Palm up bent hands move alternately up and down. Also means **BALANCE, SCALES**.

WELL, FINE, HEALTH/Y

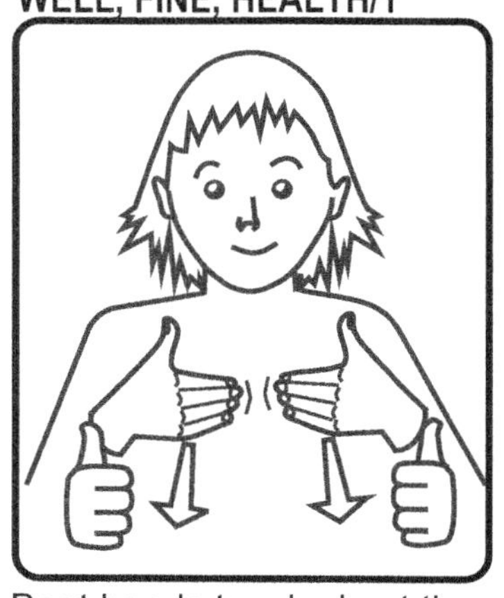

Bent hands touch chest then move forward closing with thumbs up. With raised brows means **ARE YOU WELL?**

WEST

R. flat hand with fingers pointing up, moves to the left.

WET, DAMP, MOIST

Fingers of bent hand open and close onto thumb several times. Two hands can be used.

WHALE

Fingers of palm forward full 'O' hand on head spring upwards and open several times. Both hands can be used. ***Varies.***

WILD, UNTAMED

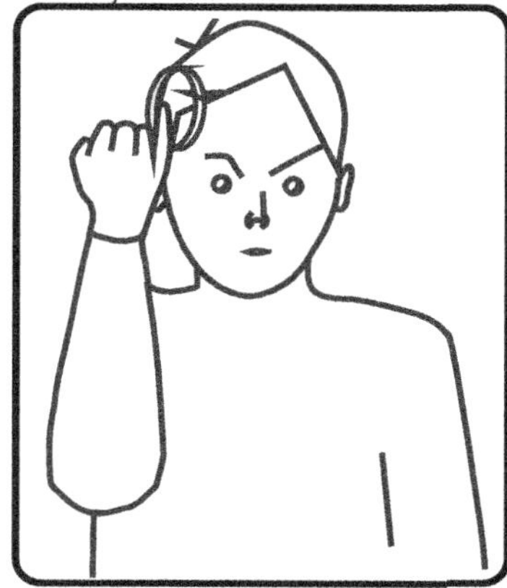

Extended little finger makes circular movements on side of forehead.

WIND, WINDY, GUSTY

Palm back open hands fan back to face several times, or in ***direction*** to suit context.

WINDMILL

L. flat hand held with fingers pointing up; R. index finger moves in large circular motions around L. hand.

WINGS, FLY

Open hands make small flapping movements at sides of shoulders. Also one version of **BAT**.

WIRE

Palm forward 'O' hands held together move apart.

WOOD

Tip of R. extended thumb brushes L. palm twice, twisting upwards from the wrist.

WOOL

Palm facing clawed hands touch then pull apart closing to bunched hands and repeat.

WORLD, EARTH

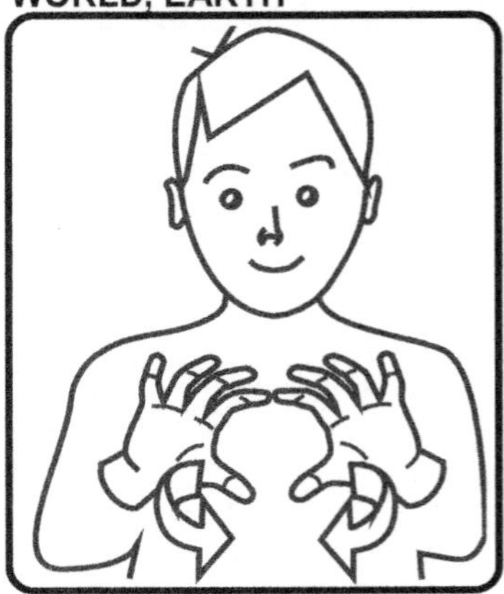

Open hands with fingers slightly curved twist round, down and apart in spherical shape. Also means **PLANET, SPHERE.**

WRONG, FAULT

Edge of R. little finger bangs down (may repeat) on L. palm or directed towards referent or can be fingers wiggling palm back on chin.

X-RAY

(General sign) Fingerspell 'X' then with indexes pointing backwards, outline frame on chest or fingerspell in full.

X-RAY

Fingerspell 'X' then full 'O' hand springs open (**RADIATE, SHINE**) on appropriate part of the body.

YEAR, YEARS

Hands form fingerspelt 'Y' with small downward brushing movement. Also one version of **YOUNG.** Repeat for **YEARS.**

ZYGOTE

(When sperm fertilises egg a zygote is formed) Fingers of 'O' hands interlock (**JOIN**) then clawed hands held together, twist open slightly.

USEFUL RESOURCES AND CONTACTS

Action on Hearing Loss
19-23 Featherstone Street,
London EC1Y 8SL
Information line:
Tel: 0808 808 0123 (freephone)
Textphone: 0808 808 9000 (freephone)
email:informationline@hearingloss.org.uk
web: www.actiononhearingloss.org.uk

British Association of Teachers of the Deaf (BATOD)
National Executive Officer and
Magazine Editor:
Paul Simpson
Tel: 0845 6435181
email: exec@batod.org.uk
web: www.batod.org.uk

British Deaf Association
BDA Head Office
2nd Floor, 356 Holloway Road
London N7 6PA
Tel: 020 7697 4140
email: bda@bda.org.uk
web: www.bda.org.uk

Special iApps
Educational apps for children who are deaf and those with learning disabilities such as autism and Down syndrome
Tel: 0191 375 7903
email: support@specialiapps.co.uk
web: www.specialiapps.co.uk

Co-Sign Communications
(inc. DeafBooks & Deafsign)
For the Let's Sign Series
Stockton-on-Tees TS18 5HH
Tel: 01642 580505
email: info@deafbooks.co.uk
web: www.deafbooks.co.uk
email: cath@deafsign.com
web: www.deafsign.com

The National Deaf Children's Society (NDCS)
Ground Floor South, Castle House,
37-45 Paul Street
London EC2A 4LS
Fax: 020 7251 5020
Switchboard Tel: 020 7490 8656
email: ndcs@ndcs.org.uk
web: www.ndcs.org.uk

Signature
Mersey House, Mandale Business Park,
Belmont, Durham DH1 3UZ
Tel: 0191 383 1155 **Text**: 07974 121594
Fax: 0191 383 7914
email: enquiries@signature.org.uk
web: www.signature.org.uk

Symbols Worldwide Ltd T/A Widgit Software
26 Queen Street, Cubbington,
Leamington Spa CV32 7NA
Tel: 01926 333680 **Fax:** 01926 885293
email: info@widgit.com
web: www.widgit.com

USEFUL WEBSITES

www.mybslbooks.com
www.bbc.co.uk/seehear
www.bslsignbank.ucl.ac.uk
www.signbsl.com
www.signstation.org
www.bslzone.co.uk
www.batod.org.uk
www.signature.org.uk

SCIENCE sign vocabulary websites

www.sciencesigns.ac.uk/home_glossary.asp
www.ssc.education.ed.ac.uk/bsl/list.html

INDEX

D

E

F

G

H

I

J

Printed in Great Britain
by Amazon

76252492R00059